It's another great book from CGP...

Chemistry exams can seem daunting — especially if you're not sure what to expect.
But they're less stressful if you've done plenty of realistic practice in advance.

Happily, this book (which includes a **free** Online Edition)
is packed with exam-style questions for every topic. It even includes
two complete practice exams to fully prepare you for the real thing.

How to get your free online edition

Want to read this book on your computer or tablet?
Just go to **cgpbooks.co.uk/extras** and enter this code...

0590 0369 7167 6068

By the way, this code only works for one person. If somebody else has used
this book before you, they might have already claimed the online edition.

What CGP is all about

Our sole aim here at CGP is to produce the highest quality books —
carefully written, immaculately presented and dangerously close to being funny.

Then we work our socks off to get them out to you
— at the cheapest possible prices.

Contents

✓ Use the tick boxes to check off the topics you've completed.

Section 1 — Principles of Chemistry

Section 2 — Chemistry of the Elements

Section 3 — Organic Chemistry

Section 4 — Physical Chemistry

Section 5 — Chemistry in Industry

Practice Papers

> **How to get answers for the Practice Papers**
> Your free Online Edition of this book includes all the answers for Practice Papers 1C & 2C.
> (Just flick back to the previous page to find out how to get hold of your Online Edition.)

Published by CGP

Editors:
Jane Applegarth, Katherine Craig, Mary Falkner, Ben Fletcher, Christopher Lindle.

Contributors:
Michael Aitken, Max Fishel, Paddy Gannon, Anne Hetherington.

With thanks to Chris Elliss, Glenn Rogers and Karen Wells for the proofreading.
With thanks to Jonathan Schofield for the reviewing.

ISBN: 978 1 84762 693 6

Groovy website: www.cgpbooks.co.uk

Jolly bits of clipart from CorelDRAW®
Printed by Elanders Ltd, Newcastle upon Tyne

Based on the classic CGP style created by Richard Parsons.

How to Use This Book

- Hold the book <u>upright</u>, approximately <u>50 cm</u> from your face, ensuring that the text looks like <u>this</u>, not sᴉɥʇ. Alternatively, place the book on a <u>horizontal</u> surface (e.g. a table or desk) and sit adjacent to the book, at a distance which doesn't make the text too small to read.

- In case of emergency, press the two halves of the book together <u>firmly</u> in order to close.

- Before attempting to use this book, familiarise yourself with the following <u>safety information</u>:

The questions are arranged into topics, so you can get exam practice on exactly the bit of your course that you want.

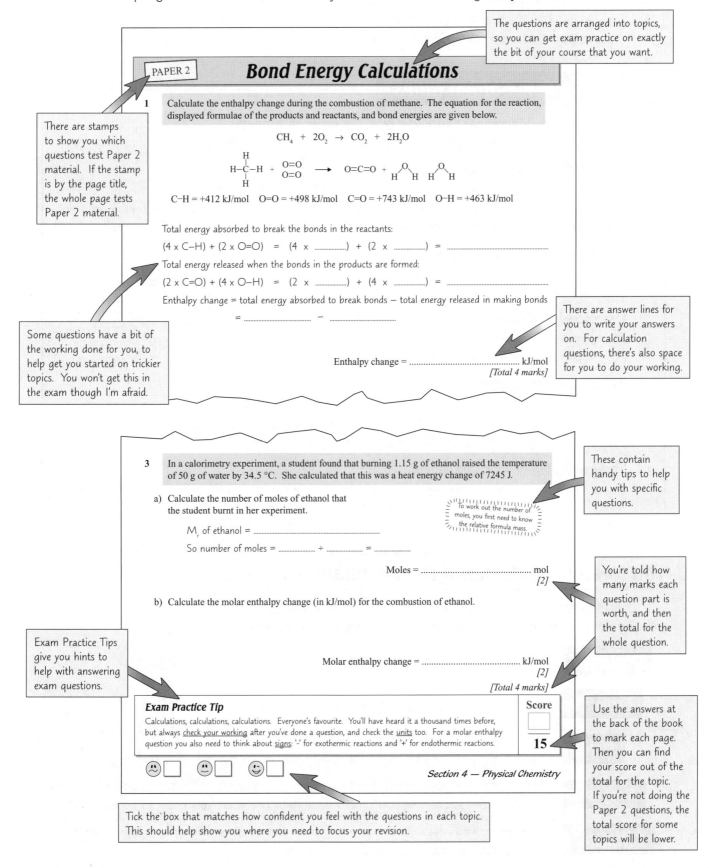

PAPER 2

Bond Energy Calculations

1. Calculate the enthalpy change during the combustion of methane. The equation for the reaction, displayed formulae of the products and reactants, and bond energies are given below.

There are stamps to show you which questions test Paper 2 material. If the stamp is by the page title, the whole page tests Paper 2 material.

$$CH_4 + 2O_2 \rightarrow CO_2 + 2H_2O$$

C–H = +412 kJ/mol   O=O = +498 kJ/mol   C=O = +743 kJ/mol   O–H = +463 kJ/mol

Total energy absorbed to break the bonds in the reactants:

(4 x C–H) + (2 x O=O) = (4 x ....) + (2 x ....) = ...

Total energy released when the bonds in the products are formed:

(2 x C=O) + (4 x O–H) = (2 x ....) + (4 x ....) = ...

Enthalpy change = total energy absorbed to break bonds − total energy released in making bonds

= .... − ....

Some questions have a bit of the working done for you, to help get you started on trickier topics. You won't get this in the exam though I'm afraid.

Enthalpy change = ... kJ/mol

[Total 4 marks]

There are answer lines for you to write your answers on. For calculation questions, there's also space for you to do your working.

3. In a calorimetry experiment, a student found that burning 1.15 g of ethanol raised the temperature of 50 g of water by 34.5 °C. She calculated that this was a heat energy change of 7245 J.

These contain handy tips to help you with specific questions.

a) Calculate the number of moles of ethanol that the student burnt in her experiment.

M_r of ethanol = ...

So number of moles = ... ÷ .... = ...

To work out the number of moles, you first need to know the relative formula mass.

Moles = ... mol

[2]

b) Calculate the molar enthalpy change (in kJ/mol) for the combustion of ethanol.

You're told how many marks each question part is worth, and then the total for the whole question.

Molar enthalpy change = ... kJ/mol

[2]

[Total 4 marks]

Exam Practice Tips give you hints to help with answering exam questions.

Exam Practice Tip

Calculations, calculations, calculations. Everyone's favourite. You'll have heard it a thousand times before, but always <u>check your working</u> after you've done a question, and check the <u>units</u> too. For a molar enthalpy question you also need to think about <u>signs</u>: '-' for exothermic reactions and '+' for endothermic reactions.

Score

☐

15

Use the answers at the back of the book to mark each page. Then you can find your score out of the total for the topic. If you're not doing the Paper 2 questions, the total score for some topics will be lower.

☹ ☐   ☺ ☐   ☻ ☐

Section 4 — Physical Chemistry

Tick the box that matches how confident you feel with the questions in each topic. This should help show you where you need to focus your revision.

Exam Tips

Edexcel Certificate Exam Stuff

1) You have to do two exams for the Edexcel Certificate in Chemistry — Paper 1 and Paper 2 (ingenious).
2) Paper 1 is 2 hours long and worth 120 marks.
3) Paper 2 is just 1 hour long, and it's worth 60 marks.
4) Some material in the specification will only be tested in Paper 2. The questions that cover Paper 2 material in this book are marked with a stamp.

If you're doing the International GCSE in Chemistry, it works in exactly the same way — so you'll do two papers too.

There are a Few Golden Rules

1) **Always, always, always make sure you read the question properly.**
   For example, if the question asks you to give your answer in g/dm^3, don't give it in mol/dm^3.

2) **Look at the number of marks a question is worth.**
   The number of marks gives you a pretty good clue of how much to write.
   So if a question is worth four marks, make sure you write four decent points. And there's no point writing an essay for a question that's only worth one mark — it's just a waste of your time.

3) **Write your answers as clearly as you can.**
   If the examiner can't read your answer you won't get any marks, even if it's right.

4) **Use specialist vocabulary.**
   You know the words I mean — the silly sciencey ones, like enthalpy change and polymerisation. Examiners love them.

Obeying these Golden Rules will help you get as many marks as you can in the exam — but they're no use if you haven't learnt the stuff in the first place. So make sure you revise well and do as many practice questions as you can.

5) **Pay attention to the time.**
   The amount of time you've got for each paper means you should spend about a minute per mark. So if you're totally, hopelessly stuck on a question, just leave it and move on to the next one. You can always go back to it at the end if you've got enough time.

6) **Show each step in your calculations.**
   You're less likely to make a mistake if you write things out in steps. And even if your final answer's wrong, you'll probably pick up some marks if the examiner can see that your method is right.

You Need to Understand the Command Words

Command words are the words in a question that tell you what to do.
If you don't know what they mean, you might not be able to answer the questions properly.

Describe... This means you need to recall facts or write about what something is like.

Explain... You have to give reasons for something or say why or how something happens.

State... This means the same thing as 'Name...' or 'Give...'.
You usually just have to give a short definition or an example of something.

Suggest... You need to use your knowledge to work out the answer. It'll often be something you haven't been taught, but you should be able to use what you know to figure it out.

Calculate... This means you'll have to use numbers from the question to work something out.
You'll probably have to get your calculator out.

States of Matter

1   The photograph shows a vessel in a distillery. The walls of the vessel are solid copper.

   a)   Use words from the box to complete the sentences about solids.
       Each word may be used once, more than once or not at all.

       [4]

weak	move	colder	hotter	random
strong	expand	heavier	dissolve	regular

       In solids, there are .... forces of attraction between particles,

       which hold them in fixed positions in a .... arrangement.

       The particles don't .... from their positions, so solids keep their shape.

       The .... the solid becomes, the more the particles in the solid vibrate.

   b)   Inside the vessel, liquid ethanol is turned into ethanol gas. Describe the changes in arrangement,
       movement and energy of the particles when the liquid ethanol is heated to become a gas.

       ....

       ....

       ....

       [3]

       [Total 7 marks]

2   The diagram shows a substance changing
   between solid, liquid and gas states.

   a)   Give the letter of the arrow that represents **subliming**.

       ....

       [1]

   b)   Give the name of the process represented by arrow A. ....

       [1]

   c)   Describe what happens to the particles in a solid when it is heated to the point of melting.

       ....

       ....

       ....

       ....

       [4]

       [Total 6 marks]

       Score: ⬚

       13

⊗ ⬚   ⊙ ⬚   ☺ ⬚

Movement of Particles

1   A student placed a small amount of potassium manganate(VII) in a beaker of water.
    The potassium manganate(VII) completely dissolved, turning the water nearby purple.
    Eventually all the water in the beaker was purple.

a) Give the name of the process which made the colour spread through the beaker.

    ....
                                                                                                    [1]

b) The student then added more water to the beaker. Place a cross in the box by the sentence that
    correctly explains what happened to the colour of the water.

    ☐   The colour was unchanged as the amount of potassium manganate(VII) stayed the same.

    ☐   The colour was unchanged as water particles don't react with potassium manganate(VII).

    ☐   The water got less purple as some of the potassium manganate(VII) particles reacted.

    ☐   The water got less purple as the potassium manganate(VII) particles spread further apart.
                                                                                                    [1]

c) The result of the student's next experiment is shown below. A white ring of ammonium chloride
    has formed on the glass tube at the point where the hydrogen chloride gas met the ammonia gas.

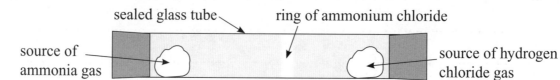

    Place a cross in the box by the sentence that correctly explains why the ring formed closer to the
    source of hydrogen chloride than the source of ammonia.

    ☐   The air was warmer near the source of the hydrogen chloride, so it evaporated more quickly.

    ☐   The particles of ammonia are smaller and lighter, so they diffused more quickly.

    ☐   The particles of ammonia were diluted by the air in the tube.

    ☐   The particles of hydrogen chloride gas vibrated about a fixed position.
                                                                                                    [1]
                                                                                        [Total 3 marks]

2   In the experiment shown in the diagram, a gas jar full of brown
    bromine gas is separated from a gas jar full of air by a glass plate.

    The glass plate is then removed.
    Describe and explain the appearance of the gas jars after an hour.

    bromine

    ....

    ....   glass plate

    ....
                                                                                        [2]   air
                                                                                [Total 2 marks]   Score: ☐

5

☹ ☐   😐 ☐   ☺ ☐

Atoms

1 Atoms are made up of protons, neutrons and electrons.

a) State the number of protons, neutrons and electrons in an atom of fluorine.

fluorine is $^{19}_{9}F$ so the total number of protons and neutrons is ....

and the total number of protons is ....

so there are .... − .... = ... neutrons.

The number of electrons = the number of .... so it contains .... electrons.

Protons ....   Neutrons ....   Electrons ....

[2]

b) Complete the table.

Particle	Relative mass	Charge
Proton	....	+1
Neutron	1	....
Electron	....	−1

[3]

c) State the name for a group of atoms held together by covalent bonds ....

[1]

[Total 6 marks]

2 This question is about helium.

a) Give the atomic number and mass number of helium.

Atomic number ....

Mass number ....

[1]

b) What is the name for the part of the atom below that is shaded grey? ....

[1]

c) This diagram of an atom of helium is incomplete.
Complete the diagram using:
● to represent electrons,
■ to represent protons, and
× to represent neutrons.

[3]

[Total 5 marks]

Exam Practice Tip

There's no nice way to say this, but if you can't answer questions like these, you'll struggle later on. You really, really need to know this stuff — so it's worth taking some time now to make sure you've got it all straight. If you need to, go back and do some more revision so that you can ace these questions next time round.

Score

11

Elements, Compounds and Mixtures

1   Many everyday substances, such as copper, are elements.
Other substances, such as table salt, are compounds.

Briefly describe the difference between an element and a compound.

....

....

[Total 2 marks]

2   The photograph shows the NASA Space Shuttle soon after being launched.

a)   The two booster rockets contain solid fuel, which is a mixture of mostly aluminium (Al) and
ammonium perchlorate (NH_4ClO_4).

Complete the table using words from the list below.
Each word may be used once, more than once, or not at all.

solid fuel   **aluminium**   **aluminium perchlorate**

Property	Substance
Consists of one type of atom only.	....
Contains different chemicals which can be separated using physical methods.	....
Made of two or more different elements which are chemically bonded.	....

[3]

b)   The large central tank contains liquid oxygen and liquid hydrogen.
In the shuttle's thrusters, oxygen reacts with hydrogen to produce water vapour.

i) Is liquid oxygen an element, compound or mixture?   ....

[1]

ii) Is water vapour an element, compound or mixture?   ....

[1]

[Total 5 marks]

Score:

7

Section 1 — Principles of Chemistry

Separating Mixtures

1 A forensic scientist is using paper chromatography to compare different inks.

a) Describe the method used to set up a paper chromatography experiment to compare the inks.

....

....

....

....

....

....

[3]

b) The scientist is using paper chromatography to compare an ink used on a document with the ink in three different printers. The chromatogram is shown on the right.

Which printers could **not** have produced the document?

....

[1]

[Total 4 marks]

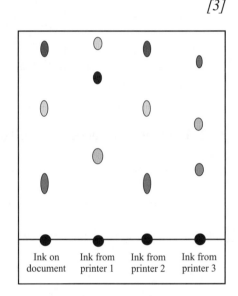

Ink on document   Ink from printer 1   Ink from printer 2   Ink from printer 3

2 Lawn sand is a mixture of insoluble sharp sand and soluble ammonium sulfate fertiliser.

a) Describe how you would obtain pure, dry samples of the two components in the lab.

....

....

....

....

[4]

b) A student separated 51.4 g of lawn sand into sharp sand and ammonium sulfate.
After separation, the total mass of the two products was 52.6 g. Suggest **one** reason for this error.

....

....

[1]

[Total 5 marks]

3 The boiling points of three liquids are shown in the table.

a) State why simple distillation cannot be used to separate water from a solution of water and methanoic acid.

....

....

[1]

Liquid	Boiling point (°C)
Methanoic acid	101
Propanone	56
Water	100

b) The apparatus shown was used to separate a mixture of propanone and water. Use the options from the list below to complete the table. Each option may be used once, more than once, or not at all.

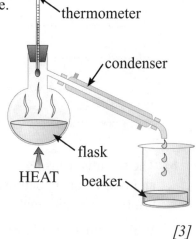

| no liquid | water | propanone | both liquids |

Temperature on thermometer	Contents of the flask	Contents of the beaker
30 °C	....	....
65 °C	....	....
110 °C	....	....

[3]

c) Explain how fractional distillation works to separate a mixture of liquids.

....

....

....

....

....

[4]

[Total 8 marks]

4 Different groups of seaweed contain different types of a pigment called chlorophyll.

The table below shows which types of chlorophyll each group of seaweed contains.

Group of seaweed	Type of chlorophyll		
	a	b	c
Red	✓		
Brown	✓		✓
Green	✓	✓	

Use the chromatogram to identify which group the unknown seaweed belongs to.

....

[Total 1 mark]

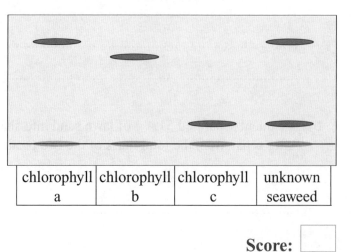

| chlorophyll a | chlorophyll b | chlorophyll c | unknown seaweed |

Score: ☐

18

☹ ☐   😐 ☐   🙂 ☐

The Periodic Table and Electron Shells

1 The periodic table contains all the elements arranged in order.

a) How are the elements arranged in the periodic table?
Put a cross in the appropriate box to indicate your answer.

☐ By atomic number

☐ By electron number

☐ By mass number

☐ By neutron number

[1]

b) How can you deduce the number of electrons in the outer shell of an element from its position in the periodic table?

....

....

[1]

[Total 2 marks]

2 The diagram shows some of the elements in the periodic table.

Group 1	Group 2											Group 3	Group 4	Group 5	Group 6	Group 7	Group 0
	Be											B	C	N	O	F	
	Mg											Al			S		
K	Ca																Kr

Write the symbol of an element shown in the diagram that:

a) has seven outer electrons ....
[1]

b) has a full outer electron shell ....
[1]

c) has the electronic configuration 2, 8, 6 ....
[1]

d) has one outer electron ....
[1]

[Total 4 marks]

10

3 Beryllium and calcium are both Group 2 elements.

a) Give the electronic configuration of beryllium. ....

[1]

b) The diagram shows the incomplete electron arrangement of a calcium atom.
Complete the diagram to show the electron arrangement of a calcium atom.

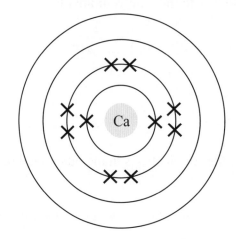

[2]

c) Calcium can react with oxygen to produce calcium oxide.
How many extra electrons does an atom of oxygen need to fill up its outer shell?

....

[1]

[Total 4 marks]

4 The electronic configuration of an atom shows how many electrons there are in each energy level.

a) An atom has the electronic configuration 2, 8, 8, 1. Identify which element the atom is.

....

[1]

b) The diagram on the right incorrectly shows the electronic configuration of neon.
 i) State what is wrong with the first energy level in the diagram.

 ....

 ....

 [1]

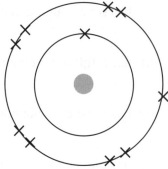

 ii) State what is wrong with the second energy level in the diagram.

 ....

 ....

 [1]

[Total 3 marks]

Score:

13

10

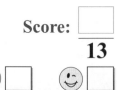

Ionic Bonding

1 Magnesium reacts with sulfur to produce magnesium sulfide.

a) In this reaction, magnesium atoms become magnesium ions.

State what happens when magnesium ions are formed, in terms of loss or gain of electrons. Give the name for this type of reaction.

What happens to magnesium atoms ....

....

Type of reaction ....

[2]

b) When they react with sodium, sulfur atoms each gain two electrons. When chlorine atoms react with sodium, they each gain only one electron. Explain this difference.

....

....

....

[2]

[Total 4 marks]

2 Potassium nitrate and potassium chloride are used as fertilisers.

a) Potassium chloride (KCl) is an ionic compound containing potassium ions bonded to chloride ions.

i) Name the force that holds the ions together in an ionic compound. State if it is weak or strong.

Name ....

Strength ....

[2]

ii) The electronic configuration of potassium is 2, 8, 8, 1. Deduce the formula of a potassium ion.

....

[1]

iii) The electronic configuration of chlorine is 2, 8, 7. Deduce the formula of a chloride ion.

....

[1]

b) Potassium nitrate (KNO_3) is also an ionic compound.
It contains potassium ions bonded with nitrate ions (NO_3^-).

Explain why nitrate ions cannot form ionic compounds with bromide ions.

....

....

[2]

[Total 6 marks]

3 When aluminium is extracted from aluminium oxide, the aluminium oxide is dissolved so that the aluminium ions it contains are free to move. These ions are then reduced to give aluminium atoms.

a) The electronic configuration of aluminium is 2, 8, 3. Deduce the formula of an aluminium ion.

....

[1]

b) State, in terms of electrons, what is meant by reduction.

....

....

[1]

c) Oxide ions are also formed when aluminium oxide is dissolved.
Give the formula of an oxide ion. ....

[1]

d) Three of the diagrams below incorrectly show the formation of an oxide ion from an oxygen atom.

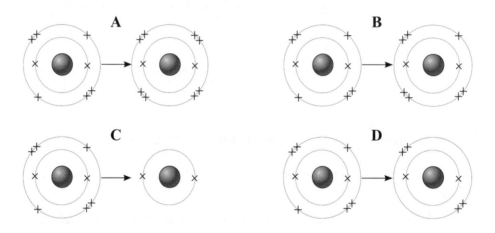

Which diagram correctly shows the formation of an oxide ion? ....

[1]

[Total 4 marks]

4 The incomplete table shows the electronic configurations of some elements and the formulae of the ions that they form.

Complete the table.

Element	Electronic configuration	Formula of ion formed
Lithium	2, 1	Li$^+$
....	2, 8, 8, 2	....
Sodium	2, 8, 1	....
....	2, 7	F$^-$

[Total 4 marks]

Score: ☐

18

☹ ☐ ☺ ☐ ☺ ☐

Ionic Compounds

1   Sodium chloride is an ionic compound.

a) Choose words from the box to complete the sentences below. Each word may be used once, more than once, or not at all.

| strong | negative | large | positive | weak | high | low | small |

Sodium chloride has very .... electrostatic forces of attraction between

the .... sodium ions and the .... chloride ions.

This means that it needs a .... amount of energy to break the bonds,

and so its melting point is ....

[5]

b) Draw a dot and cross diagram for the ions in sodium chloride, including the charge on each ion. Only show the outer electrons.

[3]

c) The diagram below shows the ions in a different ionic compound. All of the electrons are shown.

Identify the positive and negative ions in this compound.

From the dots and the crosses, you can see that the positive ion has lost three electrons. So you can use the periodic table to work out what atom it was to start with. Do the same for the negative ions.

Positive   ....

Negative   ....

[2]

[Total 10 marks]

2 Different compounds have different melting points.

a) The melting point of calcium chloride is **772 °C** and that of carbon chloride is **–23 °C**.
State which compound is an ionic compound, and explain your answer.

Compound ....

Explanation ....

....

....

[3]

PAPER 2

b) Sodium chloride and magnesium oxide are both ionic compounds.
State which compound you would expect to have a higher melting point, and explain your answer.

Compound ....

Explanation ....

....

....

....

[3]

PAPER 2

c) The melting point of sodium chloride is related to its structure.

i) Briefly describe the structure of sodium chloride and how it is held together.

....

....

[2]

ii) Which of the diagrams, **A**, **B** or **C**, correctly represents the structure of sodium chloride?

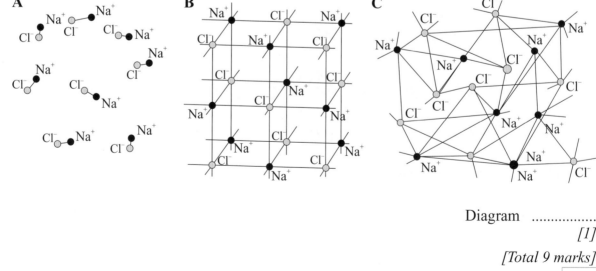

Diagram ....

[1]

[Total 9 marks]

Score: ⬜

19

Covalent Bonding

1   The bonding in phosphorus trichloride (PCl_3) is shown in the dot-and-cross diagram.
Only the outer electrons are shown.

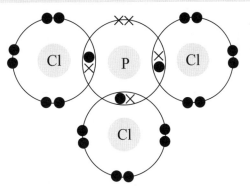

a)   State how many electrons there are in the outer shell of each atom in PCl_3 ....
                                                                                                        [1]

b)   State how many shared pairs of electrons there are in a molecule of PCl_3 ....
                                                                                                        [1]

c)   State how many double covalent bonds there are in a molecule of PCl_3 ....
                                                                                                        [1]

                                                                                              [Total 3 marks]

2   Dot and cross diagrams can be used to show the position of electrons in covalent molecules.

a)   Complete the dot and cross diagrams for the molecules below. Only show the outer electrons.

   i) hydrogen chloride, HCl   ii) oxygen, O_2 iii) ammonia, NH_3

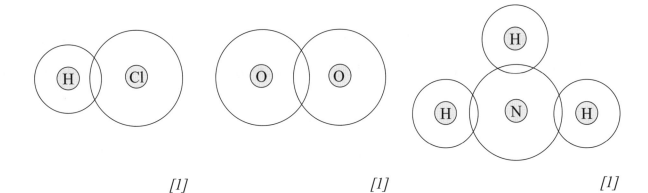

                   [1]   *[1]*   *[1]*

b)   Explain how the atoms are held together in a molecule of hydrogen chloride.

   ....

   ....

   ....

   ....
                                                                                                        [2]

                                                                                              [Total 5 marks]

3 Hydrocarbon gases such as propane (C_3H_8) and ethane (C_2H_6) are useful chemicals. The dot and cross diagram shows the arrangement of the outer shell electrons in propane.

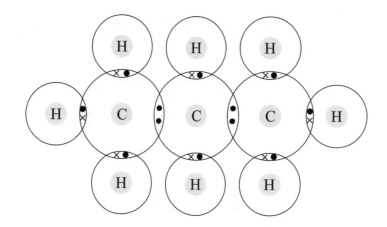

Draw a dot and cross diagram of ethane. Only show the outer electrons of each atom.

[Total 2 marks]

4 The atoms in hydrogen sulfide (H_2S) are bonded in a similar way to the atoms in water (H_2O).

Draw a dot and cross diagram of hydrogen sulfide. Only show the outer electrons of each atom.

[Total 2 marks]

Score:

12

Covalent Substances

1 The table below shows the properties of four substances.

Substance	Melting point (°C)	Conducts electricity when a liquid
A	−102	no
B	1085	yes
C	993	yes
D	1650	no

a) State and explain which substance could be silicon dioxide, a giant covalent substance.

Substance ....

Explanation ....

....

[2]

b) State and explain which substance could be chlorine, a simple molecular substance.

Substance ....

Explanation ....

....

[2]

[Total 4 marks]

2 Hydrogen and chlorine share electrons to form a molecule called hydrogen chloride.

Put a cross in the appropriate box to indicate whether hydrogen chloride will have a low or high boiling point.

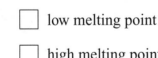 low melting point

high melting point

Explain your answer.

....

....

....

[Total 2 marks]

18

3   Silicon carbide has a giant covalent structure and is a solid at room temperature.

Explain, in terms of its bonding and structure, why silicon carbide has a high melting point.

....

....

....

[Total 2 marks]

PAPER 2

4   Graphite and diamond are both entirely made from carbon, but have different properties.

a) Why does the structure of graphite make it a useful lubricant?

....

....

....

[2]

b) Explain why diamond's structure makes it useful as a cutting tool.

....

....

....

[2]

c) The diagrams below show the arrangement of atoms in four molecules.

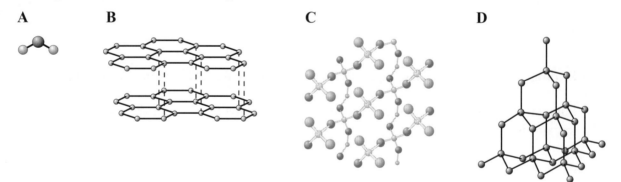

A   **B**   **C**   **D**

Choose from the letters **A-D** to answer the questions below.

i) Which diagram shows the arrangement of atoms in graphite?   ....

[1]

ii) Which diagram shows the arrangement of atoms in diamond?   ....

[1]

[Total 6 marks]

Score: ⬜

14

Section 1 — Principles of Chemistry

Balancing Equations

1 Methane (CH_4) burns in oxygen (O_2) to make carbon dioxide (CO_2) and water (H_2O).

a) State the names of the reactants and products in this reaction.

Reactants .... Products ....

[2]

b) Write a word equation for this reaction.

....

[1]

c) Write a balanced chemical equation for this reaction.

....

[2]

[Total 5 marks]

2 Carbon monoxide can form in poorly-ventilated gas fires.
Below is an equation for this reaction, which is incorrectly balanced.

$$C + O_2 \rightarrow CO$$

Identify which one of the following equations is balanced correctly.
Place a cross in the appropriate box to indicate your answer.

☐ $C + O_2 \rightarrow CO_2$

☐ $C + O_2 \rightarrow 2CO$

☐ $2C + O_2 \rightarrow 2CO$

[Total 1 mark]

3 Acids can react with a variety of different metals and their oxides.

a) Balance the following chemical equations.

i) ....HCl + ...CuO → ....$CuCl_2$ + ...H_2O

ii) ....HNO_3 + ...MgO → ....$Mg(NO_3)_2$ + ...H_2O

> Not every compound will need a number in front of it to balance the equations.

[2]

b) Write a balanced chemical equation for the reaction of hydrochloric acid (HCl) with aluminium (Al) that produces aluminium chloride ($AlCl_3$) and hydrogen (H_2).

....

[2]

[Total 4 marks]

Section 1 — Principles of Chemistry

4 A more reactive halogen can displace a less reactive halogen from a solution of its salt.

Write a balanced chemical equation for the reaction of chlorine (Cl_2) with potassium bromide (KBr). The products of this reaction are bromine (Br_2) and potassium chloride (KCl).

....

[Total 2 marks]

5 Reduction reactions involve the removal of oxygen from a compound.

a) Balance the following equation, which shows the reduction of iron oxide.

$$........CO + ...Fe_2O_3 \rightarrow ....CO_2 + ...Fe$$

[1]

b) Balance the following equation, which shows the reduction of copper oxide.

$$........CuO + ...C \rightarrow ....Cu + ...CO_2$$

[1]

[Total 2 marks]

6 Sodium (Na) is a reactive alkali metal, which is found in Group 1 of the periodic table.

a) Sodium reacts with chlorine (Cl_2) to form sodium chloride (NaCl).

Write a balanced chemical equation for this reaction.

....

[2]

b) When a solution of calcium hydroxide ($Ca(OH)_2$) is mixed with solid sodium carbonate (Na_2CO_3), sodium hydroxide solution (NaOH) and a precipitate of calcium carbonate ($CaCO_3$) are produced.

The equation for the reaction is:

$$Ca(OH)_2(........) + Na_2CO_3(........) \rightarrow 2NaOH(........) + CaCO_3(........)$$

Complete the equation by adding state symbols.

[1]

c) Solid sodium metal reacts with water to form a solution of sodium hydroxide (NaOH). Hydrogen (H_2) is also given off.

Write a balanced chemical equation for this reaction, including state symbols.

....

[3]

[Total 6 marks]

Exam Practice Tip

It's important that you get to grips with balancing equations because it often features in exam papers. Remember to double check your equation after you've balanced it and you'll be on to a winner. You need to make sure you know your state symbols too, because they come hand-in-hand with chemical equations.

Score

[ ]

20

Isotopes and Relative Atomic Mass

1 Two of the most common isotopes of chlorine are chlorine-35 (^{35}Cl) and chlorine-37 (^{37}Cl).

a) State what is meant by the term **isotope**.

....

....

....

[2]

b) Complete the following table to show the mass number and the numbers of protons and neutrons in each of these chlorine isotopes.

Isotope	Mass number	Number of protons	Number of neutrons
^{35}Cl	35	17	
^{37}Cl			

[2]

c) The relative abundances of ^{35}Cl and ^{37}Cl are shown in the table below.

Isotope	Relative abundance
^{35}Cl	75%
^{37}Cl	25%

i) What is meant by the term **relative atomic mass**?

....

....

....

[2]

ii) Use the information in the table to work out the relative atomic mass of chlorine.

Relative atomic mass = ...

[3]

[Total 9 marks]

Exam Practice Tip

Definitions can be tricky to remember but it's worth learning them because they are a good way of picking up easy marks. Just keep writing them down until they are stuck in your head. The definitions of isotopes and relative atomic mass are a good place to start. So what are you waiting for — get scribbling....

Score

_____

9

Relative Formula Mass

1   A solution of calcium hydroxide, $Ca(OH)_2$ can be known as limewater.

Calculate the relative formula mass of calcium hydroxide, $Ca(OH)_2$.

Relative formula mass = ...

[Total 2 marks]

2   A scientist has been given some information to work out the identity of some elements.

> Element **W** has an A_r of 4.
>
> Element **X** has an A_r 3 times that of element **W**.
>
> Element **Y** has an A_r 4 times that of element **W**.

You'll need to use the periodic table to help you answer this question. You'll get one in the exam too.

a)   Identify the elements **W**, **X** and **Y**.

Element **W**: ....   Element **X**: ....   Element **Y**: ....

[3]

b)   The scientist is then given the chemical formula and relative formula mass (M_r) of an unknown compound which contains another unknown element, **Z**, as shown below.

Chemical formula = $\mathbf{Z_2XY_3}$ $M_r = 106$

Use the information above to answer the following questions.

i)   Calculate the A_r of **Z**.

A_r of Z = ...

[3]

ii) Identify the element **Z**.

....

[1]

[Total 7 marks]

3   The equation below shows a reaction between an unknown element, **A**, and water.
The total M_r of the products is 114.

$$2\mathbf{A} + 2H_2O \rightarrow 2\mathbf{A}OH + H_2$$

Identify element **A**.

Element A = ...

[Total 3 marks]

Score: ☐

12

☹ ☐   😐 ☐   ☺ ☐

Empirical and Molecular Formulae

1 Nitrogen monoxide, NO, reacts with oxygen, O_2, to form oxide **R**.

A 100 g sample of oxide **R** contains 30.4 g of nitrogen and 69.6 g of oxygen.
Work out the empirical formula of oxide **R**.

Empirical formula = ...

[Total 3 marks]

2 A compound contains 10.1% aluminium and 89.9% bromine by mass.

Calculate the empirical formula of the compound.

Empirical formula = ...

[Total 3 marks]

3 1.48 g of a calcium compound contains 0.8 g calcium and 0.64 g of oxygen. The rest is hydrogen.

Work out the empirical formula of the compound.

Empirical formula = ...

[Total 4 marks]

4 A molecule has an empirical formula of C_3H_7O, and a relative molecular mass of 118.

Deduce the molecular formula of the molecule.

Molecular formula = ...

[Total 3 marks]

Score:

13

Calculating Masses in Reactions

1 A student is investigating the combustion of metals.

a) The student burns 10 g of magnesium in air to produce magnesium oxide (MgO).

$$2Mg + O_2 \rightarrow 2MgO$$

Calculate the maximum mass of magnesium oxide that could be produced in the reaction.

Mass of magnesium oxide = ... g

[3]

b) Using the chemical equation below, work out the mass of sodium
that the student would need to burn in order to produce 2 g of sodium oxide.

$$4Na + O_2 \rightarrow 2Na_2O$$

Mass of sodium = ... g

[3]

[Total 6 marks]

2 Aluminium and iron oxide (Fe_2O_3) react together to produce aluminium oxide (Al_2O_3) and iron.

$$2Al + Fe_2O_3 \rightarrow Al_2O_3 + 2Fe$$

a) What is the maximum mass of iron that can be produced from 20 g of iron oxide?

Mass of iron = ... g

[3]

b) What is the maximum mass of aluminium that will react with 32 kg of iron oxide?

Don't get caught out by
changes in the units — part b)
was in g, but part c) is in kg.

Mass of aluminium = ... kg

[3]

[Total 6 marks]

3   Iron oxide is reduced to iron inside a blast furnace using carbon.
There are three stages involved. The equations for these three stages are shown below.

$$Stage\ 1:\quad C_{(s)} + O_{2(g)} \rightarrow CO_{2(g)}$$

$$Stage\ 2:\quad CO_{2(g)} + C_{(s)} \rightarrow 2CO_{(g)}$$

$$Stage\ 3:\quad 3CO_{(g)} + Fe_2O_{3(s)} \rightarrow 3CO_{2(g)} + 2Fe_{(l)}$$

If 10 g of carbon are used in stage 2, and all the carbon monoxide produced gets used in stage 3, what mass of CO_2 is produced in stage 3?

Firstly, mass of CO produced from 10 g of C at stage 2:

C

12

12 ÷ .... = ... g

.... × 10 = ... g

2CO

2 × (12 + 16) = 56

56 ÷ .... = ... g

.... × 10 = ... g

Secondly, mass of CO_2 made from .... g of CO at stage 3:

3CO

3 × (12 + 16) = 84

84 ÷ .... = ... g

.... × .... = ... g

3CO$_2$

3 × [12 + (16 × 2)] = 132

132 ÷ .... = ... g

.... × .... = ... g

Mass of CO_2 = ... g

[Total 6 marks]

4   Sodium sulfate (Na_2SO_4) is made by reacting sodium hydroxide (NaOH) with sulfuric acid (H_2SO_4). Water is another product of this reaction.

$$2NaOH + H_2SO_4 \rightarrow Na_2SO_4 + 2H_2O$$

a)   What mass of sodium hydroxide is needed to make 75 g of sodium sulfate?

Mass of sodium hydroxide = ... g

[3]

b)   What is the maximum mass of water that can be formed when 50 g of sulfuric acid reacts with sodium hydroxide?

Mass of water = ... g

[3]

[Total 6 marks]

Exam Practice Tip

It's really important to get your head around the method for calculating masses in reactions. It's just a case of finding the relative molecular masses for the bits that you want, and then doing a spot of dividing and multiplying. And don't forget to double check your working to make sure your answer is right.

Score

24

Percentage Yield

1   A teacher wanted to produce some silver chloride (AgCl). The teacher added a carefully measured mass of silver nitrate to an excess of dilute hydrochloric acid. 1.2 g of silver chloride were produced.

   a) Explain what is meant by the **yield** of a chemical reaction.

....

[1]

   b) i) State the formula for calculating the percentage yield of a reaction.

....

[1]

       ii) The teacher calculated that he should get 2.7 g of silver chloride from the reaction. What was the percentage yield?

Percentage yield = ...

[1]

[Total 3 marks]

2   Solutions of barium chloride and sodium sulfate were mixed together in a beaker to produce barium sulfate. The solution was filtered to obtain the solid barium sulfate.

The reaction was predicted to give a yield of 15 g of barium sulfate. However, after the experiment was completed a yield of only 6 g had been obtained. Calculate the percentage yield.

Percentage yield = ...

[Total 1 mark]

3   The reaction between magnesium and oxygen produces a white powder, magnesium oxide. Three samples of magnesium, each weighing 2 g, were burned and the oxide produced was weighed. The expected yield was 3.33 g.

Complete the following table with the percentages yields of the three samples.

Sample	Mass of oxide (g)	Percentage yield
A	3.18	
B	3.05	
C	3.15	

[Total 3 marks]

Score: ☐

7

Moles

1 A scientist measured out one mole of iron into a beaker.

You'll have a periodic table in your exam which you can look at any time. You might find it useful for the questions on this page.

a) What is the mass of one mole of iron?

....

[1]

b) What is the name given to the particular number of particles equal to one mole of a substance?

PAPER 2 ....

[1]

[Total 2 marks]

2 A student was asked to calculate the number of moles and the masses of different compounds she would be using in her lab practical.

a) State the formula used to work out the number of moles from the mass of a substance.

....

[1]

b) Calculate the number of moles in the following substances.

   i) 14 g of lithium   ....

   ii) 112 g of sulfur   ....

   iii)390 g of silicon dioxide (SiO_2) ....

   iv)275 g of zinc carbonate ($ZnCO_3$) ....

[4]

c) Calculate the masses of the following molar quantities of substances.

   i) 1 mole of nickel   ....

   ii) 2 moles of aluminium   ....

   iii)6 moles of hydrochloric acid ....

   iv)4.5 moles of copper oxide (CuO) ....

[4]

[Total 9 marks]

3 A teacher has a 140 g sample of potassium hydroxide (KOH).

Calculate how much more KOH the teacher needs to have a 4 mole sample.

Extra KOH needed = ... g

[Total 2 marks]

Score: ☐

13

☹ ☐ ☺ ☐ ☺ ☐

Water of Crystallisation

1 Na$_2$CO$_3$.xH$_2$O is a hydrated salt, which means that water molecules are present in the lattice structure. This water is called water of crystallisation.

By heating a sample of a hydrated salt you can gradually remove the water of crystallisation to form an anhydrous salt. This can be done by placing a sample of the hydrated salt into a crucible and gently heating it using a Bunsen burner.

A student used this method to remove the water of crystallisation from Na$_2$CO$_3$.xH$_2$O to produce the anhydrous salt Na$_2$CO$_3$. The student put a sample of Na$_2$CO$_3$.xH$_2$O into a crucible, weighed both together, and recorded the mass. The student then heated the sample for 2 minutes, left it to cool and recorded the mass of the sample and crucible again. The student repeated this until two separate masses that had the same value were recorded. The student made a note of this mass.

The student recorded the following masses:

Starting mass of crucible + Na$_2$CO$_3$.xH$_2$O	61.224 g
Final mass of crucible + Na$_2$CO$_3$	56.364 g

a) What is the purpose of heating the hydrated salt until the mass remains constant?

....

[1]

b) The mass of the crucible was 53.500 g.
Use this to calculate the masses of the following samples.

   i) Na$_2$CO$_3$.xH$_2$O

   ....

[1]

   ii) Na$_2$CO$_3$

   ....

[1]

c) The relative formula mass of water is 18.

Calculate the relative formula mass of Na$_2$CO$_3$ and use this along with your answers to part b) to work out the value of x in Na$_2$CO$_3$.xH$_2$O.

x = ...

[4]

[Total 7 marks]

Score:

7

Moles, Volume and Concentration

1   The volume that one mole of a gas occupies at room temperature and pressure is called its molar volume.

PAPER 2

    a)   State the value of the molar volume of a gas.

     ....

                             [1]

    b)   i)   What volume does 1.5 moles of hydrogen take up?

                            Volume = ... dm^3

                                        [1]

       ii) How many moles are there in 2250 cm^3 of ammonia (NH_3)?

                          Number of moles = ...

                                          [1]

    c)   Find the volume of carbon dioxide produced (at room temperature and pressure) when 6.9 g of carbon is completely burned in oxygen.

$$C + O_2 \rightarrow CO_2$$

                            Volume = ... dm^3

                                        [4]

                             [Total 7 marks]

2   Sodium hydroxide (NaOH) reacts with sulfuric acid to produce sodium sulfate (Na_2SO_4) and water.

    a)   How many moles of sodium hydroxide are in 125 cm^3 of a 2.5 mol/dm^3 solution?

                          Number of moles = ...

                                          [1]

    b)   What is the concentration of a solution with 3 moles of sodium sulfate in 750 cm^3?

                          Concentration = ... mol/dm^3

                                        [1]

    c)   Give your answer for part b) in g/dm^3.

                          Concentration = ... g/dm^3

                                        [2]

                             [Total 4 marks]

Score:

11

Electrical Conductivity

1 An experiment was carried out to find out if the ionic compound magnesium oxide conducts electricity. The compound was tested when it was solid, dissolved in water and molten.

a) Complete the table of results.

State	Conducts electricity? (yes/no)
Solid	....
Dissolved in water	....
Molten	....

[3]

b) Explain your answers to part a).

....

....

....

[2]

c) To conduct electricity a compound must be able to carry an electric current.
Explain what is meant by the term **electric current**.

....

[1]

d) Explain why most covalent compounds don't conduct electricity.

....

....

[2]

[Total 8 marks]

2 Metals are held together by metallic bonding.

a) Metallic bonding occurs due to the structure of a metal. Describe the structure of a metal.

....

....

[1]

b) Metals are good conductors of electricity and most are malleable.
Explain why metals have these properties by referring to metallic structure and bonding.

....

....

....

[2]

[Total 3 marks]

Score:

11

Electrolysis

1   The diagram below shows the electrolysis of lead bromide.

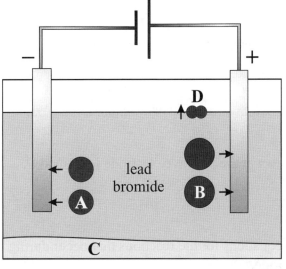

a)   Choose from the letters **A**, **B**, **C** or **D** to identify the following substances on the diagram.

Pb^{2+} ....   molten lead   ....

Br^- .... Br_2 ....

[2]

b)   Write balanced half-equations for the processes that occur during the electrolysis of lead bromide.

Negative electrode: ....

Positive electrode: ....

[4]

c)   In electrolysis, a liquid ionic substance such as lead bromide is needed to conduct electricity and allow current to flow around the electrolytic cell.

   i) State the name given to these conductive substances.   ....

[1]

   ii) Describe an experiment to test whether a particular substance can be used for this purpose.

   ....

   ....

   ....

[2]

   iii)Lead bromide is an ionic substance which doesn't easily dissolve in water.
       How could it be made into a liquid for electrolysis?

   ....

[1]

[Total 10 marks]

2 Electrolysis using inert electrodes can be carried out with several different aqueous solutions.

PAPER 2

a) An aqueous solution of sodium chloride (NaCl) is being electrolysed.

i) Predict the products formed in this reaction and give their states.

Negative electrode:

Product: .... State: ....

Positive electrode:

Product: .... State: ....

[4]

ii) Explain why the product at the negative electrode is formed.

....

[1]

iii) Write balanced half-equations for the reactions that occur during the electrolysis of aqueous sodium chloride.

Negative electrode: ....

Positive electrode: ....

[4]

b) Write balanced half-equations for the reactions that occur during the electrolysis of an aqueous solution of sulfuric acid. State the electrode at which each reaction occurs.

Half-equation: .... Electrode: ....

Half-equation: .... Electrode: ....

[5]

c) An aqueous solution of copper sulfate ($CuSO_4$) can undergo electrolysis.

i) State the **four** ions that this solution contains.

1 .... 2 ....

3 .... 4 ....

[4]

ii) Predict the products formed at each electrode.

Negative electrode: ....

Positive electrode: ....

[3]

[Total 21 marks]

Exam Practice Tip

Electrolysis. It might seem like witchcraft, but it does all actually make sense if you work it out bit-by-bit. Make sure you know which reaction occurs at each electrode, and get super confident at writing out lovely correctly-balanced half-equations, and you'll be well on the way to being an electrolysis genius.

Score

31

| PAPER 2 | *Electrolysis — Calculating Masses* |

1 The amount of product formed in electrolysis depends on the number of electrons transferred.

Complete the table to show the amounts required to produce 1 mole of each metal from its ion.

Metal ion	Number of moles of electrons	Number of faradays
Ca^{2+}	....	....
K^+	....	....
Al^{3+}	....	....

[Total 6 marks]

2 A student is carrying out some calculations associated with electrolysis.

a) What charge has moved when 3.2 A has flowed for 20 seconds?

Charge = ... C

[1]

b) Calculate the time in minutes that 6 A needs to flow for to provide a charge of 4320 coulombs.

Time = ... minutes

[2]

[Total 3 marks]

3 Molten silver nitrate was electrolysed for 40 minutes using a current of 0.2 amps.

The half-equation for the reaction is: $Ag^+ + e^- \rightarrow Ag$

a) Calculate the number of faradays that flowed during the electrolysis. Take the value of 1 faraday to be 96 000 coulombs.

Time must be in seconds for these calculations.

Number of faradays = ... F

[2]

b) How many moles of silver were deposited at the negative electrode?

Number of moles = ... mol

[1]

c) Calculate the mass of silver deposited at the negative electrode.

Mass = ... g

[2]

[Total 5 marks]

Score:

14

Section 2 — Chemistry of the Elements
More About the Periodic Table

1   The diagram on the right shows the position of the element bismuth in the periodic table.

line **A**

Bi

a)   What is the name for a row of elements in the periodic table?

   ....
   [1]

b)   Barium oxide was dissolved in water. What was the pH of the solution? Place a cross in **one** box.

   ☐ less than 7   ☐ 7   ☐ greater than 7

   [1]

c)   Element **X** is found in the same group of the periodic table as bismuth.

   i)   What does that tell you about the two elements' properties?

   ....
   [1]

   ii) Element **X** does not conduct electricity. Predict whether element **X** will be found to the left or the right of line **A** in the diagram above. Explain your answer.

   ....

   ....
   [2]

   [Total 5 marks]

2   The periodic table contains many patterns in the properties of the elements.

a)   Place a cross in **one** box to show which pair of elements have similar properties.

   ☐ C and O   ☐ He and F   ☐ Ca and Mg   ☐ Si and Br

   [1]

b)   Explain why sodium and potassium undergo similar reactions with water.

   ....

   ....
   [1]

c)   Explain why Group 0 elements are unreactive.

   ....

   ....
   [2]

   [Total 4 marks]

   Score: ☐

   9

☺☐   ☺☐   ☺☐

Group 1 — The Alkali Metals

1   A teacher dropped small, similar sized pieces of three different alkali metals, **A**, **B** and **C**, into water. The students recorded the time taken for each piece to react completely.

Metal	Time taken to react (s)
A	27
B	8
C	42

a) State which of these metals, **A**, **B** or **C**, is the most reactive. Explain how you know.

Metal .... Explanation ....

....
[2]

b) The three metals used were lithium, sodium and potassium.
   Use the results shown in the table to match them up to the correct letters **A**, **B** and **C**.

A = ...   **B** = ...   **C** = ...
[2]

c) What products would be formed in a reaction between sodium and water?

....
[2]

d) One of the students said "The amount of time taken for rubidium to react with water would be shorter than for metal **A**, but longer than for metal **B**".

Why is the student incorrect?

....

....
[2]

[Total 8 marks]

PAPER 2

2   Explain why alkali metals become more reactive as their atomic number increases.

....

....

....

[Total 3 marks]

Exam Practice Tip
Chemistry is full of patterns, so if you come across one make sure you learn the reason behind it — not only will it help you to remember the pattern, it might well get you some marks in the exam. If you're doing Paper 2, one to make sure you know is the reason why reactivity changes as you go down a group.

Score

11

🙁 ☐   😐 ☐   🙂 ☐

Group 7 — The Halogens

1 The properties of the elements within Group 7 change as you go down the group.

a) Complete the table to show the colour of chlorine and the physical state of iodine at 25 °C.

Element	Atomic number	Colour	Boiling point (°C)	Physical state at 25 °C
chlorine	17	....	−34	gas
bromine	35	red-brown	59	liquid
iodine	53	dark grey	185	....

[2]

b) Fluorine is another Group 7 element.

   i) How would you expect the reactivity of fluorine to compare to the reactivity of chlorine?

   ....

   [1]

   ii) Predict the physical state of fluorine at 25 °C

   ....

   [1]

   [Total 4 marks]

2 Chlorine gas and hydrogen gas can react together to make hydrogen chloride.

a) Write a balanced chemical equation for this reaction. Include state symbols.

   ....

   [3]

b) Some of the product of this reaction is dissolved in water.
   The rest of the product is dissolved in methylbenzene (an organic solvent).

   i) Explain, in terms of dissociation, the difference in the **acidity** of these two solutions.

   ....

   ....

   ....

   ....

   [4]

   ii) Name the solution formed when hydrogen chloride gas dissolves in water.

   ....

   [1]

   [Total 8 marks]

Score:

12

Displacement Reactions

1 Halogens can take part in displacement reactions with halogen salts.

a) State what is meant by the term **displacement reaction**.

....

....
[1]

b) When bromine water is added to potassium iodide solution a reaction will take place.

i) Write a symbol equation for the reaction.

....
[2]

ii) Explain why this reaction happens.

....

....

....
[2]

c) The reaction of bromine water with potassium iodide solution is a redox reaction.

i) State what is meant by the term **redox reaction**.

....

....
[1]

ii) Identify the substance which acts as an oxidising agent when bromine water is added to potassium iodide.

....
[1]

[Total 7 marks]

If you're struggling with part c) ii), try using the equation you wrote in part b) i) to help you work out what's losing electrons and what's gaining electrons.

2 When chlorine water is added to a solution of potassium bromide, a chemical reaction occurs. State the colour of the solution before and after the reaction.

Before ....

After ....
[2]

[Total 2 marks]

Score:

9

Reactions of Metals and the Reactivity Series

1 Four different metals are reacted with dilute sulfuric acid.
The diagram below shows the reactions after 30 seconds.

A — unknown metal B — iron C — aluminium D — magnesium, gas syringe, dilute $H_2SO_{4(aq)}$

a) i) Name the **two** products of reaction **C**.

1 ....

2 ....

[2]

ii) Describe a simple test that you could perform to confirm the identity of the gas
collected from reaction **C**.

....

....

[2]

b) Write the letters **A-D** to arrange the reactions
from least vigorous to most vigorous going left to right.

Least vigorous   →   **Most vigorous**

Reaction .... → Reaction .... → Reaction .... → Reaction ....

[2]

c) Use your knowledge of the reactivity series and your answer to part b) to suggest which metal is
the unknown metal in the diagram above.

Write out part of the reactivity series...

More reactive: Magnesium
                Aluminium
                Zinc
                Iron
Less reactive: Copper

unknown metal: ....

[1]

d) Complete the word equation for the reaction of sodium with water.

sodium + water → .... + ...

[2]

[Total 9 marks]

2 A student placed pieces of copper, zinc and an unknown metal in zinc sulfate solution and copper sulfate solution and left them for an hour. The student's results are shown below.

	zinc	copper	unidentified metal
reaction with zinc sulfate	no reaction	no reaction	no reaction
reaction with copper sulfate	reaction	no reaction	reaction

a) Suggest the name of the unidentified metal.

....

[1]

Writing out the reactivity series on a spare bit of paper will help with this question.

b) Explain how you can tell that the unidentified metal is more reactive than copper.

....

[1]

[Total 2 marks]

3 A student performed an investigation to observe the chemical reactions of four metals with some metal oxides. The student's results are displayed in the table below. The student put a tick if a reaction occurred and a cross if there was no reaction.

	aluminium oxide	copper oxide	iron oxide	magnesium oxide
aluminium	✓	✓	✓	✗
copper	✗	✗	✗	✗
iron	✗	✓	✗	✗
magnesium	✓	✓	✗	✗

a) Two results in the table are wrong.
Find and circle the **two** incorrect results.

[2]

b) State how many of the oxides in the table you would expect to react with gold. ....

[1]

c) Which metal in the table would you expect to react most vigorously with copper oxide?
Give a reason for your answer.

Metal ....

Reason ....

....

[2]

[Total 5 marks]

Iron

1   In an experiment to investigate rusting, three iron nails were placed into separate test tubes.

boiled (airless) water →   **A**

air →   tap water →   **B**

air →   cotton wool →   drying agent →   **C**

a)   State the **two** things that are needed for iron to rust.

1 ....   2 ....

[2]

b)   In which tube, **A**, **B** or **C**, will the nail rust? ....

[1]

c)   Rusting is an oxidation reaction. State what is meant by the term **oxidation**.

....

[1]

d)   Experiment B was repeated, but using a nail that had first been coated in paint.
      Suggest what you would observe in this experiment and explain your prediction.

....

....

[2]

e)   One method of protecting iron nails from rusting is coating with zinc.

i)   What is the name for this method of protection? ....

[1]

ii) Explain how this method prevents iron from rusting even if the coating is scratched
     to reveal the iron underneath.

....

....

[2]

f)   What is the best method of preventing moving parts from rusting? Put a cross in **one** box.

☐ Plastic coating   ☐ Sacrificial magnesium blocks   ☐ Oiling   ☐ Painting

[1]

[Total 10 marks]

Exam Practice Tip

If you're told "Put a cross in **one** box", you may not be surprised to know that putting a cross in more than one box will not get you any marks. But if you realise you've gone wrong — pause to check you really mean to change your answer, then write next to the question a clear explanation of what you meant to put.

Score

☐

—

10

Oxygen in the Atmosphere

1   This pie chart shows the composition of the Earth's atmosphere, excluding water vapour.

a) Complete the labels on the pie chart.

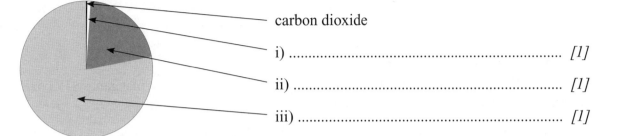

carbon dioxide

i) .... *[1]*

ii) .... *[1]*

iii) .... *[1]*

b) Give the approximate percentages of the following gases in the air:

i) nitrogen ....   ii) carbon dioxide ....

[1]   *[1]*

[Total 5 marks]

2   The proportion of oxygen in the atmosphere can be found by heating an excess of copper so that it reacts with oxygen in the air to form copper oxide.

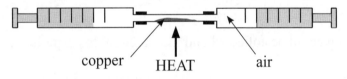

copper   HEAT   air

There was 50 cm^3 of dry air in the apparatus at the start of the experiment. How much air would be in the apparatus at the end of the experiment?

Air is ....% oxygen

100% – ....% = ...%

50 cm^3 × .... = ...cm^3 Volume of air = ... cm^3

[Total 2 marks]

3   An experiment is set up to investigate what percentage of the air is made up of oxygen. The apparatus used is shown on the right.

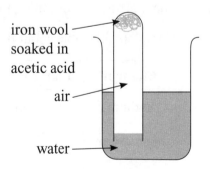

iron wool soaked in acetic acid

air

water

The student found that at the beginning of the experiment the test tube contained 28.0 cm^3 of air. At the end of the experiment the test tube contained 21.7 cm^3 of air.

Use these results to calculate the percentage of oxygen in air.

Percentage of oxygen in air = ... %

[Total 2 marks]

Score:

9

Oxygen in Reactions

1   Oxygen can be produced by the decomposition of hydrogen peroxide (H_2O_2).

a) Write a chemical equation for the decomposition of hydrogen peroxide, including state symbols.

....

[2]

b) An experiment was set up to investigate which substance is the most effective catalyst for the decomposition of hydrogen peroxide.

Samples of three substances with the same surface area were added to hydrogen peroxide solution. The same volume and concentration of hydrogen peroxide was used each time. The volume of oxygen made over time was measured and recorded, and is shown in the graph.

i) How much oxygen was produced after 3 minutes with copper(II) oxide?

Volume of oxygen = ... cm³

[1]

ii) Suggest how the oxygen could be collected and measured in this experiment.

....

[1]

iii)State, with a reason, the most effective catalyst.

Most effective catalyst ....

Reason ....

[2]

[Total 6 marks]

2   Some elements burn in air to produce oxides, which may be alkaline or acidic.

Complete this table about the reaction of certain elements with oxygen.

Element	Flame colour when burnt	Oxide formed	Acid-base character of oxide
sodium	Yellow-orange	Na_2O	Alkaline
magnesium	....	....	Slightly alkaline
carbon	Orange/yellow	CO_2	....
sulfur	....	....	....

[Total 6 marks]

Score: ☐

12

Preparation of Carbon Dioxide

1 Heating a metal carbonate, such as copper(II) carbonate, produces carbon dioxide.
This can be done in the laboratory and the carbon dioxide can be collected in a test tube.
The apparatus shown below could be used to perform this experiment.

copper(II) carbonate

test tube for collecting carbon dioxide

delivery tube

HEAT

a) The apparatus in the diagram has been set up incorrectly. Describe **one** change you would need to make in order to collect carbon dioxide and explain why this change is necessary.

....

....
[2]

b) Apart from carbon dioxide, what other product is made in this reaction?

....
[1]

c) What is the name for the type of reaction where a substance is heated and breaks down to produce two or more products?

....
[1]

[Total 4 marks]

2 Carbon dioxide can be produced from calcium carbonate and acid in the laboratory.

a) Complete the equation for the production of carbon dioxide from calcium carbonate.

$$CaCO_3 + 2\text{..............................} \rightarrow CaCl_2 + \text{..............................} + CO_2$$
[1]

b) Suggest a safety precaution that should be used when performing this reaction in the laboratory.

....
[1]

[Total 2 marks]

Score: ☐

6

Carbon Dioxide — the Good and the Bad

1 Carbon dioxide has many useful properties.

a) Use the words from the box below to complete the sentences about the uses of carbon dioxide. Each word can be used once, more than once, or not at all.

| larger   denser   oxygen   coating   very   lighter   released   hydrogen   slightly |

   i) Carbon dioxide is .... soluble in water. The bubbling when a fizzy drink bottle is

      opened is carbon dioxide escaping from the drink when the pressure is ....

                                                                                   [2]

   ii) Carbon dioxide is .... than air. It is used in some fire extinguishers.

      It stops the .... that the fire needs getting to the flames.

                                                                                    [2]

b) This experiment was used to compare the effects of nitrogen and carbon dioxide on heat radiation.

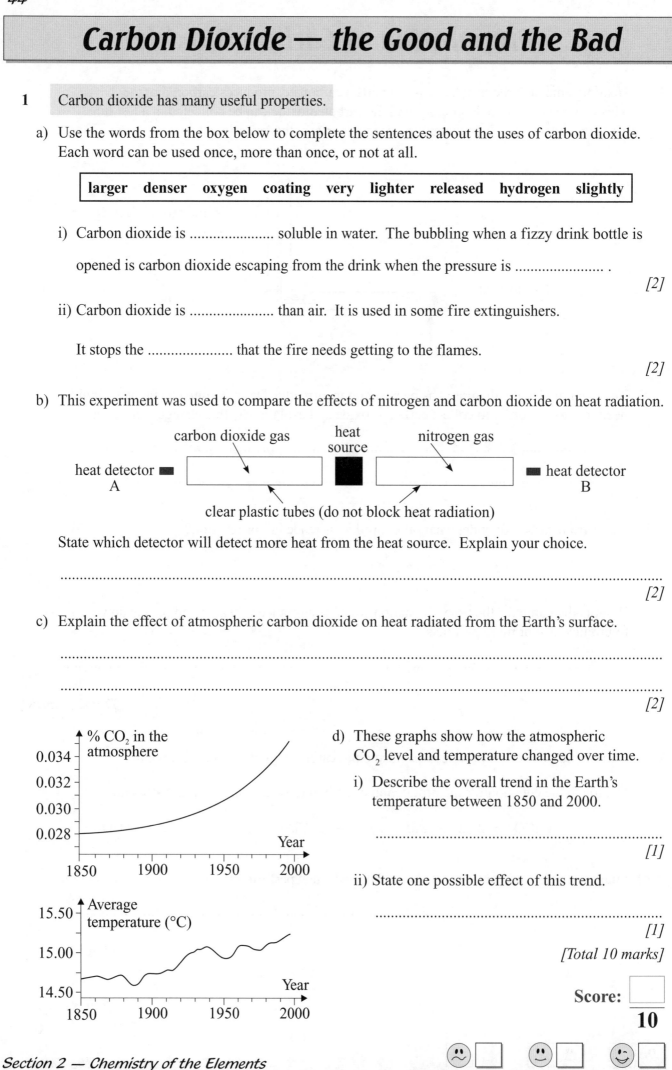

State which detector will detect more heat from the heat source. Explain your choice.

....

                                                                                    [2]

c) Explain the effect of atmospheric carbon dioxide on heat radiated from the Earth's surface.

....

....

                                                                                    [2]

d) These graphs show how the atmospheric CO_2 level and temperature changed over time.

   i) Describe the overall trend in the Earth's temperature between 1850 and 2000.

      ....

                                                [1]

   ii) State one possible effect of this trend.

      ....

                                                [1]

                                                 [Total 10 marks]

                                              Score:

                                              10

Tests for Cations

1   Potassium chloride is used to replace some of the sodium chloride in low-sodium table salt.
    A flame test can be used to tell the difference between potassium chloride and sodium chloride.

a) Describe how to carry out a flame test.

    ....

    ....

    ....
                                                                                                              [2]

b) Explain how you could tell from a flame test that a substance was potassium chloride
    and not sodium chloride.

    ....

    ....
                                                                                                              [2]

c) Some medicines contain potassium sodium tartrate.
    Explain why you cannot use a flame test to show that these medicines contained potassium.

    ....

    ....
                                                                                                              [2]
                                                                                                 [Total 6 marks]

2   A student adds a few drops of NaOH solution to solutions of different metal compounds.

a) Complete her table of results.

Metal ion	Colour of precipitate
Fe^{2+}	....
....	blue
Fe^{3+}	....

[3]

b) Complete the balanced ionic equation for the reaction of iron(II) ions with hydroxide ions by
    inserting state symbols.

$$Fe^{2+}_{(..........)} + 2OH^-_{(..........)} \rightarrow Fe(OH)_{2(..........)}$$

[1]

c) Write a balanced ionic equation for the reaction of iron(III) ions with hydroxide ions.
    Include state symbols.

    ....
                                                                                                              [3]
                                                                                                 [Total 7 marks]

Section 2 — Chemistry of the Elements

3 Tests can be used to identify positive ions.

a) Place a cross in the box to show your answer.

i) Which compound gives a crimson-red flame in a flame test?

- [ ] $CaCl_2$
- [ ] $CuSO_4$
- [ ] $LiCl$
- [ ] $(NH_4)_2SO_4$

[1]

ii) Which compound gives a brick-red flame in a flame test?

- [ ] $CaCl_2$
- [ ] $CuSO_4$
- [ ] $LiCl$
- [ ] $(NH_4)_2SO_4$

[1]

iii) Which compound forms a blue precipitate with sodium hydroxide solution?

- [ ] $CaCl_2$
- [ ] $CuSO_4$
- [ ] $LiCl$
- [ ] $(NH_4)_2SO_4$

[1]

iv) Which compound releases ammonia when sodium hydroxide solution is added?

- [ ] $CaCl_2$
- [ ] $CuSO_4$
- [ ] $LiCl$
- [ ] $(NH_4)_2SO_4$

[1]

b) Describe a test to identify ammonia gas.

....

....

....

[3]

c) State one safety precaution you would use when testing for ammonia gas in the laboratory.

....

[1]

[Total 8 marks]

Score: ☐

21

Tests for Anions

1   A student has a sample of an ionic compound and wants to find out what negative ions it contains.

a) Give the chemical formula and charge of the **negative ions** present in the following compounds.

  i) barium sulfate ....   *[1]*

  ii) potassium iodide ....   *[1]*

  iii)magnesium carbonate ....   *[1]*

b) The student wants to test the compound for the presence of sulfate ions.

  i) State which **two** reactants are used to test for sulfate ions.

     Reactant 1 ....

     Reactant 2 ....
                                                                                                   [2]

  ii) What would be observed after adding these reactants to a solution of a sulfate compound?

     ....
                                                                                                   [1]

c) The student tested the compound to see if it contained carbonate ions. The student added a
    solution to the compound, collected the gas that it gave off and bubbled the gas through limewater.

  i) Name the solution that the student added. ....
                                                                                                   [1]

  ii) The compound is a carbonate. What gas did it give off? ....
                                                                                                   [1]

d) The student is given a solution of another compound and told that it contains either
    chloride or bromide ions. Describe a test the student could perform to discover which
    of these ions it contains.

     ....

     ....

     ....
                                                                                                   [4]

e) Complete the following symbol equations for reactions involved in negative ion tests.

  i) $Ag^+ +$ .... $\rightarrow AgCl$
                                                                                                   [1]

  ii) $Ba^{2+} +$ .... $\rightarrow BaSO_4$

                                                                                                   [1]
                                                                                    [Total 14 marks]

                                                                                    Score: ☐

                                                                                    14

Tests for Gases and Water

1 Electrolysis of water gives hydrogen gas and oxygen gas.

a) Describe a simple laboratory test that you could use to identify hydrogen gas.

....

....

[2]

b) Describe a simple laboratory test that you could use to identify oxygen gas.

....

....

[2]

[Total 4 marks]

2 A fuel was burnt in pure oxygen and the products of the combustion reaction were collected.

a) A liquid condensed out of the products after they were cooled to room temperature.
The liquid was added to anhydrous copper(II) sulfate.

i) State the colour of anhydrous copper(II) sulfate powder. ....

[1]

ii) State the colour change that would take place if the liquid contained water.

....

[1]

b) The test with anhydrous copper(II) sulfate indicated that the liquid contained water.
Next, the liquid's freezing point and boiling point were found.

Freezing point: −4 °C   **Boiling point:** 106 °C

Explain what these results show.

....

....

[3]

c) The gas that was produced by the burning fuel was also tested. The gas did not bleach damp
litmus paper. When the gas was bubbled through limewater, the limewater turned cloudy.

Explain what these results show.

....

....

....

[4]

[Total 9 marks]

Score:

13

Alkanes

1   Alkanes are a group of hydrocarbon compounds.

a) State what is meant by the term **hydrocarbon**.

....

[2]

b) i) State the general formula of the alkanes.   ....

[1]

ii) Give the term for a group of compounds that can be represented by the same general formula.

....

[1]

c) Draw the displayed formula of butane.

The displayed formula just shows how all the atoms are arranged.

[1]

d) Methane will react with bromine in the presence of UV light.
    Complete the word equation for this reaction.

methane + bromine $\xrightarrow{\text{UV}}$ .... + ...

[2]

[Total 7 marks]

2   The storage tank pictured below contains butane, a saturated hydrocarbon.

a) Explain what it means when a molecule is **saturated**.

....

....

[1]

b) i) Complete the chemical equation for the complete combustion
        of butane.

.......C_4H_{10} + ... → .... + ...

[2]

ii) What other two products could be formed if butane undergoes
    incomplete combustion?

Product 1   ....

Product 2   ....

[2]

[Total 5 marks]

Score:

12

50

Alkenes

1 Alkenes are a group of unsaturated hydrocarbon molecules.

a) State the general formula of the alkenes. ....
[1]

b) Complete the table to show the missing information for the two alkenes given.

Name of alkene	Formula	Displayed formula
ethene	....	
....	C_3H_6	

[4]

[Total 5 marks]

2 Certain organic molecules can be identified using bromine water.

A	B	C	D	E

a) Diagrams **A-E** above show five different organic molecules.

i) Name molecule **C**. ....
[1]

ii) Give the letters of two isomers. .... and ....
[1]

b) Pentene is added to a tube of bromine water, and the tube is shaken.
The colour of the bromine water changes.

i) State the colour of the bromine water before and after pentene is added.

Colour before .... Colour after ....
[1]

ii) Describe what happens to pentene during this reaction.

....

....
[2]

[Total 5 marks]

Score: ☐

10

Section 3 — Organic Chemistry

PAPER 2 | **Ethanol**

1 Ethanol can be used to make ethene.

a) Write a chemical equation for the conversion of ethanol into ethene.

....

[1]

b) State the name for this type of reaction. ....

[1]

c) Identify a suitable catalyst for this reaction. ....

[1]

[Total 3 marks]

2 Two different methods can be used to manufacture ethanol.
The incomplete table below shows some information about the two methods.

a) Complete the table.

Method	Reaction	Temperature needed	Problems
A	$C_2H_4 +$ .... $\rightarrow C_2H_5OH$	....	Expensive equipment
B	$C_6H_{12}O_6 \rightarrow 2CO_2 +$ ....C_2H_5OH	....	Labour-intensive

[4]

b) What type of reaction occurs in method **B**?

....

[1]

c) Method **A** requires a high temperature.
State the pressure and type of catalyst that are typically used in the reaction.

Pressure ....

Catalyst ....

[2]

d) Country Z has a good supply of crude oil and has a very cold climate.
Suggest which method, **A** or **B**, would be most suitable for manufacturing ethanol in country Z.
Give a reason for your answer.

Method ....

Reason ....

....

[2]

[Total 9 marks]

3   Ethanol can be produced by fermentation.

a)   Fermentation is not used for large-scale production of high quality ethanol.

   i)   What chemical is reacted with steam in the large-scale production of high quality ethanol?

....

[1]

   ii) What is the raw material used to make the chemical you named in a) i)?

....

[1]

b)   There are advantages and disadvantages to using fermentation to produce ethanol.

   i)   State **one** advantage of using fermentation to produce ethanol.

....

[1]

   ii) State **one** disadvantage of making ethanol by fermentation.

....

[1]

c)   The table below shows the concentration of ethanol during a fermentation experiment.

   i)   The final three points have been plotted on the graph. Plot the first four points on the graph and draw a straight line of best fit through these four points.

[3]

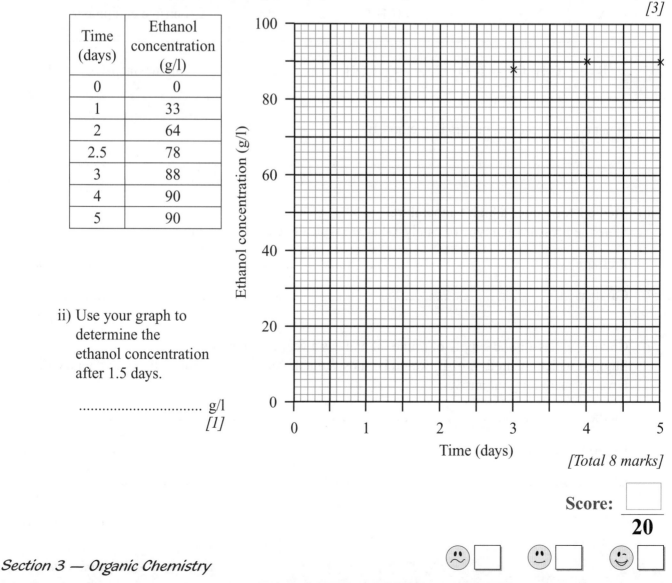

Time (days)	Ethanol concentration (g/l)
0	0
1	33
2	64
2.5	78
3	88
4	90
5	90

   ii) Use your graph to determine the ethanol concentration after 1.5 days.

.... g/l

[1]

[Total 8 marks]

Score: ☐

20

Acids and Alkalis

1   The pH scale shows how acidic or alkaline substances are.

a) What range of values does pH take? ....
[1]

b) What term is used to describe a substance with a pH of 7? ....
[1]

c) Caustic soda has a pH of around 13. Place a cross in the box that best describes caustic soda.

   ☐ strong   ☐ strong   ☐ weak   ☐ weak
       acid   alkali   acid   alkali

[1]

[Total 3 marks]

2   Bleach has a pH of around 12.
Complete the table to show what colour it would turn the following indicators.

Indicator	Colour
Litmus paper	....
Phenolphthalein	....
Universal indicator	purple
Methyl orange	....

[Total 3 marks]

3   A student has a test tube containing some acid. The student adds a few drops of universal indicator to the acid and it turns red. The student then gradually adds some alkali to the test tube.

a) What type of ions in the acid cause the indicator to become red?

....
[1]

b) What type of reaction takes place between the acid and the alkali?

....
[1]

c) The student stops adding alkali when all of the acid has reacted.
How will the student know when all of the acid has reacted?

....
[1]

[Total 3 marks]

Score: ☐

9

😕 ☐   😐 ☐   🙂 ☐

Reactions of Acids

1   Dilute acids can react with metals and with metal oxides.
    Complete the word equations for the reactions below.

a) sulfuric acid + magnesium oxide → .... + ...

[1]

b) hydrochloric acid + aluminium → .... + ...

[1]

[Total 2 marks]

2   A student is investigating the reactions of acids.

a) The student reacts nitric acid with copper oxide. Write a word equation for the reaction.

....

[1]

b) The student then adds zinc to a test tube of hydrochloric acid.
    Write a chemical equation for the reaction.

....

[2]

c) The student then reacts sodium carbonate with an acid. Sodium sulfate is formed.
    Name the acid the was used.

....

[1]

[Total 4 marks]

3   When a sample of calcium carbonate powder is placed in a
    test tube containing nitric acid, bubbles of gas are given off.

a) Name the gas evolved during the reaction.

....

[1]

b) Write a chemical equation for the reaction.

....

[2]

c) Some calcium carbonate powder is left over.
    Suggest an appropriate acid that could be added to it to make calcium chloride.

....

[1]

[Total 4 marks]

Exam Practice Tip

This topic is quite heavy on the equation front. Make sure you know what's produced when dilute acids react with metals, metal oxides or metal carbonates. For top marks you need to be super slick at balancing equations too — and there's just no substitute for practice where that's concerned.

Score

10

Making Salts

1   Use words from the box to complete the following sentences about the solubility of salts. Each word can be used once, more than once or not at all.

| soluble | alkalis | barium | acids | sodium | insoluble |

a) Most chlorides and nitrates are .... in water.

[1]

b) Soluble salts can be made by reacting .... with insoluble bases.

[1]

c) Common carbonates are .... in water. Exceptions are potassium,

ammonium and .... carbonates.

[2]

[Total 4 marks]

2   **A, B** and **C** are chemical equations for reactions in which salts are formed.

A $CuO_{(s)} + H_2SO_{4(aq)} \rightarrow CuSO_{4(aq)} + H_2O_{(l)}$

B $2NaOH_{(aq)} + H_2SO_{4(aq)} \rightarrow Na_2SO_{4(aq)} + 2H_2O_{(l)}$

C $Pb(NO_3)_{2(aq)} + H_2SO_{4(aq)} \rightarrow PbSO_{4(s)} + 2HNO_{3(aq)}$

State which equation (**A, B** or **C**) shows the formation of a salt:

a) in a reaction between an acid and an alkali. ....

b) by precipitation. ....

c) in a reaction between an acid and an insoluble base. ....

[Total 3 marks]

3   Precipitation reactions can be used to produce salts.

a) Which **two** salt solutions could you mix together to produce the salt calcium sulfate? Place crosses in the appropriate boxes to indicate your answer.

☐ calcium nitrate   ☐ barium sulfate   ☐ calcium carbonate   ☐ potassium sulfate

[2]

b) Describe how you would separate calcium sulfate from the reaction mixture after the reaction has finished.

....

[1]

[Total 3 marks]

4   Silver nitrate is a soluble salt. It can be made by adding an excess of insoluble silver carbonate to nitric acid until no further reaction occurs, as shown in the diagram.

a) Give **one** observation that would indicate that the reaction is complete.

....

....
[1]

nitric acid

excess of silver carbonate

b) Write a word equation for the reaction.

....
[1]

c) Once the reaction is complete, the excess silver carbonate can be separated from the silver nitrate solution using the apparatus shown to the right. What is this method of separation called?

....
[1]

d) Describe how you could produce solid silver nitrate from silver nitrate solution.

....
[1]

e) Potassium nitrate can be made by reacting potassium hydroxide with nitric acid.

   i) Explain why the same method used for making silver nitrate (as above) cannot be used.

   ....

   ....

   ....
   [2]

   ii) Briefly describe how you would produce a solution of pure potassium nitrate from potassium hydroxide and nitric acid.

   ....

   ....

   ....

   ....

   ....
   [3]

[Total 9 marks]

Exam Practice Tip

An exam question might rely on your knowledge of the solubility of different salts, and ask you to apply this to an unfamiliar situation. So, be sure to learn the general rules for predicting which salts are soluble — if they're firmly lodged in your brain, you'll be able to tackle whatever question the examiners throw at you.

Score

19

Titrations

1 The concentration of some limewater, $Ca(OH)_2$ solution, was determined by titration with hydrochloric acid, HCl. 50 cm³ of limewater required 20 cm³ of 0.1 mol/dm³ hydrochloric acid to neutralise it.

a) Write the chemical equation for the reaction.

....
[2]

b) Calculate the amount, in moles, of hydrochloric acid used in the reaction.

.... moles
[2]

c) Calculate how many moles of calcium hydroxide were used.

.... moles
[1]

d) Calculate the concentration of the limewater in mol/dm³.

Concentration = ... mol/dm³
[2]

e) Calculate the concentration of the limewater in g/dm³.

Concentration = ... g/dm³
[2]

[Total 9 marks]

2 In a titration, 10 cm³ of sulfuric acid was used to neutralise 30 cm³ of 0.1 mol/dm³ potassium hydroxide solution. The equation for the reaction is:
$$H_2SO_4 + 2KOH \rightarrow K_2SO_4 + 2H_2O$$

a) Calculate the concentration of the sulfuric acid in mol/dm³.

Moles of KOH = ... × (................ ÷ 1000) = ...

Reaction equation shows that .... moles of KOH react with .... moles of H_2SO_4

So .... of KOH react with .... ÷ .... = ... moles of H_2SO_4

Concentration = ... ÷ (............ ÷ 1000)

= ....

Concentration = ... mol/dm³
[5]

b) Calculate the concentration of the sulfuric acid in g/dm³.

Concentration = ... g/dm³
[2]

[Total 7 marks]

Score: ☐

16

Rates of Reaction

1 In an experiment, different sizes of marble chips were reacted with excess hydrochloric acid. The same mass of marble was used each time. The graph below shows how much gas was produced with large marble chips (X), medium marble chips (Y) and small marble chips (Z).

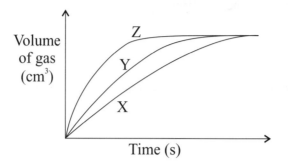

a) State and explain which curve shows the fastest rate of reaction.

Curve ....

Explanation ....

[2]

b) Why do all the reactions produce the same volume of gas?

....

[1]

The reactants were mixed in a beaker and the mass of the beaker and contents was recorded as a gas was given off. The change in mass was plotted on the graph below.

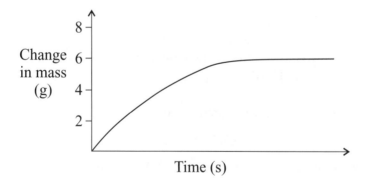

c) Does the mass of the reaction mixture increase or decrease? ....

[1]

d) On the graph, sketch the curve you would expect if the reaction was repeated:

   i) in the presence of a catalyst. Label the curve C.

   ii) at a lower temperature. Label the curve L.

   Assume all other conditions remain the same.

[2]

[Total 6 marks]

Score: ☐

6

😟 ☐   😐 ☐   🙂 ☐

Measuring Rates of Reaction

1   The rate of a reaction can be measured using different methods. If one of the products is a gas, the rate of reaction can be measured by recording the change in mass of the reaction vessel using a mass balance.

a) i) Suggest **one** advantage of measuring the change in mass using a mass balance.

....

....

[1]

ii) Suggest **one** disadvantage of this method.

....

....

[1]

b) i) Briefly describe how you could measure the rate of a reaction that produces a precipitate.

....

....

....

[2]

ii) Suggest **one** limitation of this method.

....

....

[1]

[Total 5 marks]

2   Hydrogen peroxide decomposes into water and oxygen.

a) The formula for hydrogen peroxide is H_2O_2.
Write a balanced chemical equation for the decomposition reaction.

....

[2]

b) Put a cross in the correct box to indicate which would be an appropriate method of measuring the rate of this reaction.

☐   Measuring the volume of gas produced at regular intervals.

☐   Measuring the temperature.

☐   Timing how long the reaction takes to go cloudy.

☐   Weighing the amount of water produced.

[1]

[Total 3 marks]

3 An experiment was set up to compare the rate of reaction of 5 g of magnesium ribbon with 20 ml of five different concentrations of hydrochloric acid. The volume of gas produced during the first minute of the reaction was recorded. The experiment was repeated twice for each concentration of acid. The results obtained are displayed in the table.

Concentration of HCl (mol/dm³)	Experiment 1: volume of gas produced (cm³)	Experiment 2: volume of gas produced (cm³)	Average volume of gas produced (cm³)
2	92	96	
1.5	63	65	
1	44	47	
0.5	20	50	
0.25	9	9	

a) Circle the anomalous result in the table.

[1]

b) Complete the table to show the average volume of gas produced at each concentration.

[2]

Think about what you need to do with an anomalous result when you're calculating an average.

c) i) State which concentration of hydrochloric acid produced the fastest rate of reaction.

....

[1]

ii) Explain your answer to c) i).

....

[1]

d) The apparatus used in the experiment is shown below.

X

magnesium and hydrochloric acid

i) What is the name of the piece of apparatus labelled X?

....

[1]

ii) Name **one** other piece of apparatus needed for this experiment that is not shown in the diagram.

....

[1]

e) Why did the student do the experiment twice and calculate the average volume of gas for each concentration of HCl?

....

[1]

f) Suggest **one** reason for the anomalous result.

....

[1]

[Total 9 marks]

Score:

17

Section 4 — Physical Chemistry

Rate of Reaction Experiments

1   A teacher demonstrated an experiment to investigate the effect of temperature on rate of reaction.
     The teacher added dilute hydrochloric acid at 20 °C to marble chips and measured the volume of
     gas produced at regular time intervals. The teacher then repeated the experiment at 30 °C using
     the same mass of marble chips of the same size. The results are shown below.

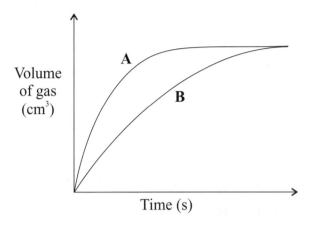

a) Which curve, **A** or **B**, shows the result of the experiment at 30 °C?

     ....
                                                                                                                    [1]

b) On the graph, sketch the curve you would expect if you repeated the experiment at 25 °C.
    Label it **C**.
                                                                                                                    [1]

c) i) State one variable that the teacher would have controlled in order to make the demonstration
        scientifically valid. Explain why this variable needed to be controlled.

        ....

        ....
                                                                                                                    [2]

    ii) Does the graph suggest that the teacher successfully controlled this variable?
        Explain your answer.

        ....

        ....
                                                                                                                    [2]

d) Which other method could be used to measure the rate of this reaction?
    Place a cross in the appropriate box to indicate your answer.

        ☐   Measuring how quickly the reaction loses mass.

        ☐   Timing how long the reaction takes to go cloudy.

        ☐   Timing how long the reaction takes to start.
                                                                                                                    [1]
                                                                                                         [Total 7 marks]

2 A student investigated the reaction between 5 g of magnesium and excess hydrochloric acid, using two different concentrations of acid. The student recorded the mass of the reaction mixture at the start and at every 10 seconds for 2 minutes, then calculated the change in mass for each reading.

a) On the axes below, sketch the curves you would expect the student to see for a high and a low concentration of acid. Label the curves.

[2]

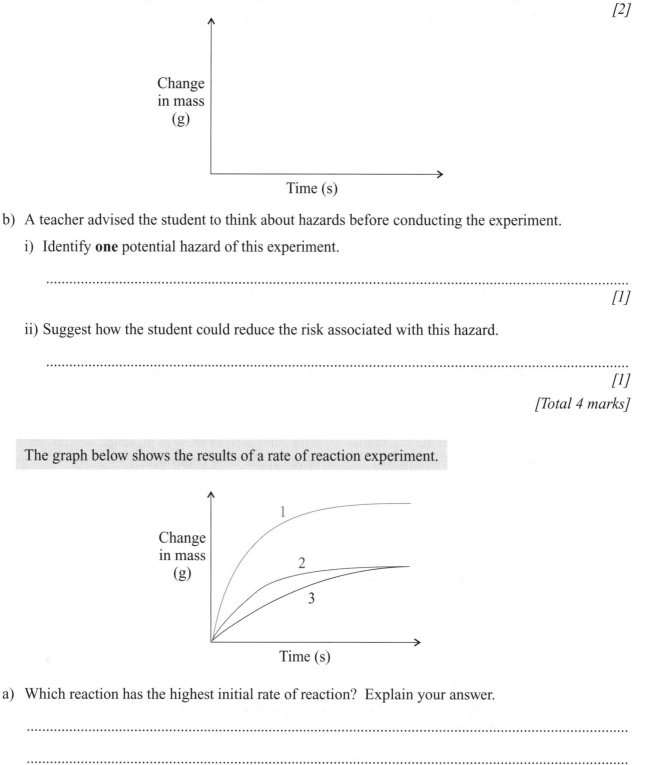

b) A teacher advised the student to think about hazards before conducting the experiment.

i) Identify **one** potential hazard of this experiment.

....

[1]

ii) Suggest how the student could reduce the risk associated with this hazard.

....

[1]

[Total 4 marks]

3 The graph below shows the results of a rate of reaction experiment.

a) Which reaction has the highest initial rate of reaction? Explain your answer.

....

....

[2]

b) Explain why all of the curves level off eventually.

....

[1]

[Total 3 marks]

4 When sodium thiosulfate solution is mixed with hydrochloric acid, a precipitate forms.

a) Suggest how you could identify when a precipitate has formed.

....
[1]

The effect of temperature on the rate of the reaction between sodium thiosulfate solution and hydrochloric acid is investigated. The reactants are mixed together in a flask and the time taken for a cross placed under the flask to disappear from view is recorded.

b) Here are the results from the experiment:

Temperature (°C)	20	30	40	50	60
Time taken for cross to disappear (s)	201	177		112	82

i) As the temperature increases, what happens to the rate of reaction?

....
[1]

ii) One of the values in the table is missing. Put a cross in the box to indicate which of the times below is most likely to be the missing value.

☐ 74 s

☐ 115 s

☐ 145 s

☐ 192 s
[1]

c) Suggest **one** way in which the reliability of the results could be improved.

....
[1]

d) A second experiment is set up to investigate the effect of varying the concentration of hydrochloric acid on the rate of reaction with sodium thiosulfate solution. The reactants are mixed together in a flask and the time taken for the cross to disappear from view is recorded. The results are displayed in the table.

Concentration of HCl (mol/dm³)	2.00	1.75	1.50	1.25	1.00
Time taken for cross to disappear (s)	13	23	38	50	67

What conclusion can be drawn from the results?

....

....
[1]

[Total 5 marks]

Section 4 — Physical Chemistry

5   A student conducted an experiment with equal masses of marble chips of the same size and equal volumes of hydrochloric acid (HCl). The student used two different concentrations of acid and measured the change in mass of the reaction mixture. The results are shown below.

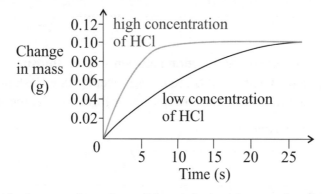

Put a cross in the box to show the valid conclusion that can be drawn from the graph:

☐   Increasing the concentration of the acid has no effect on the rate of reaction.

☐   The rate of reaction depends on the acid concentration.

☐   The rate of reaction depends on the mass of the marble chips.

[Total 1 mark]

6   The decomposition of hydrogen peroxide can be used to investigate the effect of a catalyst on the rate of a reaction. Three different catalysts are compared to see which was the most effective (increased the rate of reaction the most). A gas syringe was used to measure the amount of gas produced. Below is a graph of the results.

The three catalysts used in this experiment were potato peel, blood and manganese(IV) oxide. Manganese(IV) oxide is the most effective of these catalysts for this reaction.

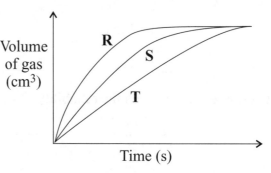

a)   Which curve, **R**, **S** or **T**, represents the reaction using a manganese(IV) oxide catalyst? Explain your answer.

     Curve .... because ....

     ....

[2]

b)   State **one** variable which must be controlled (kept constant) to ensure the experiment is valid.

     ....

[1]

[Total 3 marks]

Exam Practice Tip

It looks like there's a lot to get your head round, but really it boils down to four things: rate of reaction is increased by increasing the temperature, increasing the concentration or the surface area of the reactants, or by adding a catalyst. Learn these rules and you can apply them to any experiment you're given.

Score

☐

23

😕 ☐   🙂 ☐   😊 ☐

Collision Theory

1 Reactions occur when particles collide with each other.

a) Explain, in terms of collisions, why increasing the pressure of the reactants in a gaseous reaction increases the reaction rate.

....

....

[2]

b) Reactions only happen when particles collide with sufficient energy.

i) What is the name given to the minimum amount of energy required?

....

[1]

ii) This energy is more likely to be reached when particles are travelling faster. Suggest how the speed of particles in a reaction could be increased.

....

[1]

[Total 4 marks]

2 Magnesium carbonate is a white solid that reacts with dilute sulfuric acid to form magnesium sulfate, water and carbon dioxide.

A student conducts two experiments using magnesium carbonate and an excess of sulfuric acid. In one experiment the student uses a large chip of magnesium carbonate and in the other the same mass of powdered magnesium carbonate is used.

a) i) Which experiment will have the faster reaction rate?

....

[1]

ii) Explain your answer in terms of particle collisions.

....

....

[2]

b) The student decides that the rate of reaction is too high in one of the experiments. The student repeats the experiment using a lower concentration of acid. Explain how this will reduce the reaction rate.

....

....

[2]

[Total 5 marks]

Score:

9

Energy Transfer in Reactions

1 Use words from the box to complete the following passage about energy transfer in reactions. Each option may be used once, more than once or not at all.

less	exothermic	greater	taken in from	endothermic	given out to

Breaking bonds is an .... process and forming bonds is

an .... process. In an exothermic reaction, the energy

released during bond formation is .... than the energy

used to break the old bonds. An exothermic reaction is one in which energy is

.... the surroundings, while an endothermic reaction is

one in which energy is .... the surroundings.

[Total 5 marks]

2 During the following reaction, the temperature of the reaction mixture decreases.

$$AB + C \rightarrow AC + B$$

a) State, with a reason, whether the reaction is exothermic or endothermic.

....

....

[2]

b) Which bond is stronger, **A–B** or **A–C**? Explain your answer.

....

....

[2]

c) i) What is meant by the **enthalpy change** of a reaction?

....

[1]

ii) State whether the enthalpy change of the above reaction is positive or negative.

....

[1]

iii) Give the symbol that is used to represent enthalpy change.

....

[1]

[Total 7 marks]

3 Methane burns in oxygen to form carbon dioxide and water. The bonds in the methane and oxygen molecules break, and new bonds form to make carbon dioxide and water molecules.

a) Is energy taken in or given out when the bonds in carbon dioxide form?

....

[1]

b) Methane is a fuel commonly used in cooking and heating.
Is burning methane an endothermic or an exothermic process? Explain your answer.

....

....

[2]

c) i) Which of the following values could be the enthalpy change when one mole of methane is burnt completely in oxygen? Place a cross in the appropriate box to indicate your answer.

☐ 890.3 kJ/mol

☐ −890.3 kJ/mol

[1]

ii) Explain why you chose this value.

....

....

[1]

[Total 5 marks]

4 Ammonium chloride is a white solid that decomposes on heating to produce the gases ammonia and hydrogen chloride. The reaction is reversible, so when ammonia and hydrogen chloride are cooled, they react to form solid ammonium chloride.

$$NH_4Cl_{(s)} \rightleftharpoons NH_{3(g)} + HCl_{(g)}$$

a) Is the decomposition of ammonium chloride an exothermic or an endothermic reaction? Give a reason for your answer.

....

....

[2]

b) In a reversible reaction, the reaction in one direction is exothermic and the reaction in the other direction is endothermic. Is the enthalpy change of the reaction that forms ammonium chloride positive or negative?

....

[1]

[Total 3 marks]

Score: ☐

20

😐☐ 🙂☐ 😊☐

Section 4 — Physical Chemistry

Energy Level Diagrams

1 Chemical reactions involve enthalpy changes.

a) The enthalpy change during a reaction is +42 kJ/mol. Is the reaction exothermic or endothermic?

....

[1]

b) What is meant by the term **activation energy**?

....

[1]

c) Explain how catalysts increase the rate of a reaction.

....

[1]

[Total 3 marks]

2 The diagrams below represent the energy changes in five different chemical reactions.

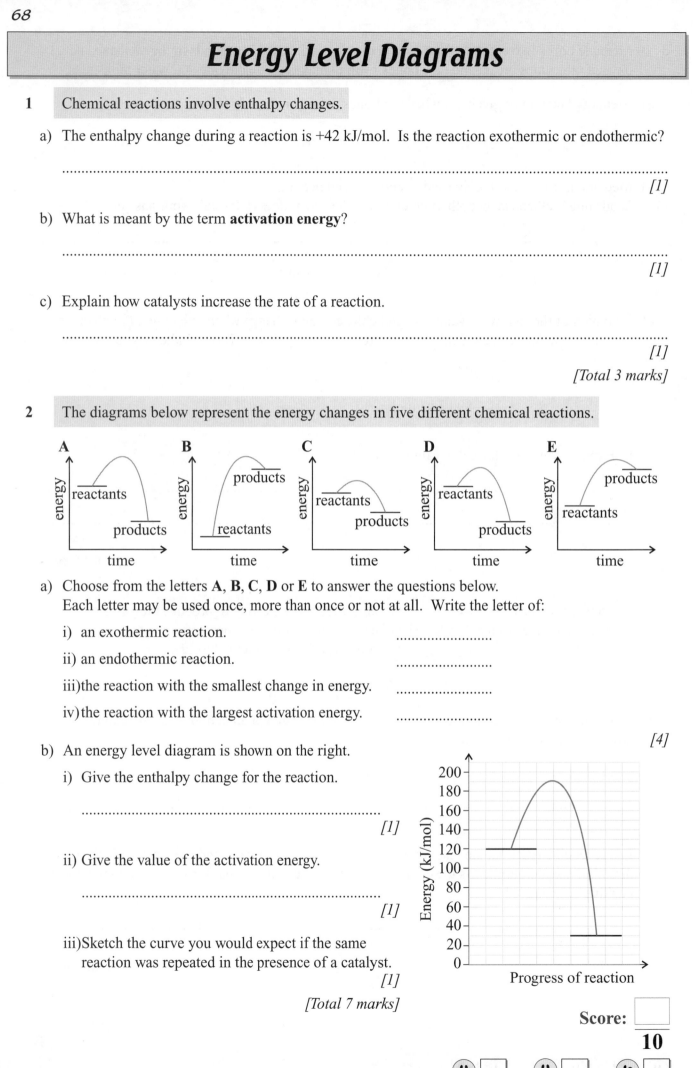

a) Choose from the letters **A**, **B**, **C**, **D** or **E** to answer the questions below.
   Each letter may be used once, more than once or not at all. Write the letter of:

   i) an exothermic reaction.   ....

   ii) an endothermic reaction.   ....

   iii) the reaction with the smallest change in energy.   ....

   iv) the reaction with the largest activation energy.   ....

[4]

b) An energy level diagram is shown on the right.

   i) Give the enthalpy change for the reaction.

   ....

   [1]

   ii) Give the value of the activation energy.

   ....

   [1]

   iii) Sketch the curve you would expect if the same
        reaction was repeated in the presence of a catalyst.

   [1]

[Total 7 marks]

Score:

10

Bond Energy Calculations

1 Calculate the enthalpy change during the combustion of methane. The equation for the reaction, displayed formulae of the products and reactants, and bond energies are given below.

$$CH_4 + 2O_2 \rightarrow CO_2 + 2H_2O$$

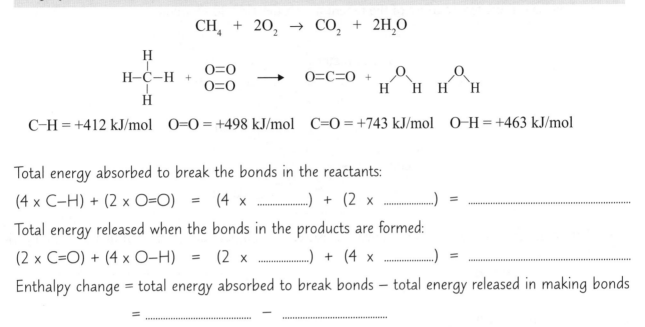

C–H = +412 kJ/mol   O=O = +498 kJ/mol   C=O = +743 kJ/mol   O–H = +463 kJ/mol

Total energy absorbed to break the bonds in the reactants:

(4 x C–H) + (2 x O=O) = (4 x ....) + (2 x ....) = ...

Total energy released when the bonds in the products are formed:

(2 x C=O) + (4 x O–H) = (2 x ....) + (4 x ....) = ...

Enthalpy change = total energy absorbed to break bonds − total energy released in making bonds

        = ... − ....

Enthalpy change = ... kJ/mol
[Total 4 marks]

2 Calculate the enthalpy change for the combustion of hydrazine, N_2H_2.
Use the equation and bond energy information given below.

$$N_2H_4 + O_2 \rightarrow N_2 + 2H_2O$$

N–N = +158 kJ/mol   N–H = +391 kJ/mol   O=O = +498 kJ/mol
           N≡N = +945 kJ/mol   O–H = +463 kJ/mol

Enthalpy change = ... kJ/mol
[Total 4 marks]

Score:

8

Section 4 — Physical Chemistry

Enthalpy Changes

1   A student investigated the temperature change during a reaction using the apparatus shown below. The student added sodium hydroxide solution to dilute hydrochloric acid, and measured the temperature of the reaction over the first 30 seconds.

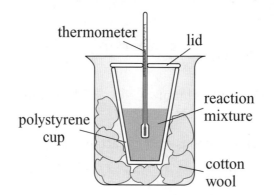

a) Before mixing the reagents, the student measured the temperature of each of them. Explain why.

....
                                                                                                                            [1]

b) State the purpose of:

   i) the cotton wool ....
                                                                                                                            [1]

   ii) the lid ....
                                                                                                                            [1]

c) The student's results are plotted on the graph shown on the right.
    What was the temperature increase during the reaction?

                                   .... °C
                                                       [1]

d) i) Suggest why it is difficult to get an accurate result for the energy change in an experiment like this.

....
                                                                                                                            [1]

   ii) How could the reliability of the results be improved?

....
                                                                                                                            [1]

e) This is a neutralisation reaction.
    Give **one** other type of reaction this method could be used to study.

....
                                                                                                                            [1]

                                                                                                      [Total 7 marks]

2 A scientist conducted a calorimetry experiment to measure the energy produced when petrol is burnt. 0.7 g of petrol was burned in a spirit burner placed underneath a copper can containing 50 g of water. The temperature of the water increased by 30.5 °C.

a) Why was a copper can chosen to hold the water?

....
[1]

b) It takes 4.2 J to raise the temperature of 1 g of water by 1 °C.
Calculate the heat energy change in the experiment using the formula:

heat energy change (J) = mass of water (g) × 4.2 × temperature change (°C)

Heat energy change = ... J
[1]

c) Use your answer to b) to calculate the energy produced per gram of petrol.
Give your answer in kJ/g.

Energy produced = ... kJ/g
[2]
[Total 4 marks]

PAPER 2

3 In a calorimetry experiment, a student found that burning 1.15 g of ethanol raised the temperature of 50 g of water by 34.5 °C. She calculated that this was a heat energy change of 7245 J.

a) Calculate the number of moles of ethanol that the student burnt in her experiment.

> To work out the number of moles, you first need to know the relative formula mass.

M$_r$ of ethanol = ...

So number of moles = ... ÷ .... = ...

Moles = ... mol
[2]

b) Calculate the molar enthalpy change (in kJ/mol) for the combustion of ethanol.

Molar enthalpy change = ... kJ/mol
[2]
[Total 4 marks]

Exam Practice Tip

Calculations, calculations, calculations. Everyone's favourite. You'll have heard it a thousand times before, but always check your working after you've done a question, and check the units too. For a molar enthalpy question you also need to think about signs: '-' for exothermic reactions and '+' for endothermic reactions.

Score

[ ]
___
15

Reversible Reactions

1   In the reaction below, substances A and B react to form substances C and D.

$$2A_{(g)} + B_{(g)} \rightleftharpoons 2C_{(g)} + D_{(g)}$$

a) What can you deduce about this reaction from the symbol $\rightleftharpoons$?

    ....

    [1]

b) What is meant by the term **dynamic equilibrium**?

    ....

    ....

    [2]

c) In the above reaction, the forward reaction is exothermic.

    i) Does the reverse reaction take in or give out heat energy? Explain your answer.

        ....

        ....

        [2]

    ii) Explain why changing the temperature of a reversible reaction always affects the position of
        the equilibrium.

        ....

        ....

        [2]

    iii)If the temperature of the above reaction is raised, will the equilibrium position move to the
        right or to the left?

        ....

        [1]

d) State and explain the effect of changing the pressure on the position of equilibrium in
    the above reaction.

    ....

    ....

    [2]

e) Ammonium chloride is heated in a beaker inside a fume cupboard to form ammonia gas and
    hydrogen chloride gas. Why can this reaction not reach equilibrium even though it is reversible?

    ....

    ....

    [1]

    [Total 11 marks]

2 When blue hydrated copper(II) sulfate is heated, steam and anhydrous white copper(II) sulfate are produced.

$$CuSO_4.5H_2O_{(s)} \rightleftharpoons CuSO_{4(s)} + 5H_2O_{(g)}$$

a) From the information given in the question, do you think the forward reaction is exothermic or endothermic. Give a reason for your answer.

....

....

[2]

b) A student has a beaker containing some anhydrous copper(II) sulfate powder. A few drops of water are added to the beaker from a pipette. Two changes are observed in the beaker.

   i) Describe what happens to the colour of the copper(II) sulfate.

   ....

   [1]

   ii) What happens to the temperature of the mixture in the beaker?

   ....

   [1]

   [Total 4 marks]

3 When ammonium nitrate is heated, it breaks down into ammonia and hydrogen chloride. The reaction is reversible.

$$NH_4Cl_{(s)} \rightleftharpoons NH_{3(g)} + HCl_{(g)}$$

Two students are trying to deduce the optimum conditions to favour the forward reaction.

The first student suggests a temperature of 375 °C and a pressure of 1 atmosphere.
The second student suggests a temperature of 250 °C and a pressure of 5 atmospheres.

Using your knowledge of equilibrium reactions, deduce which conditions are more favourable for the forward reaction. Explain your answer.

....

....

....

....

....

....

....

[Total 5 marks]

Score:

20

1 Some metals can be extracted by heating their ore with carbon.

  a) Explain why iron can be extracted from iron oxide by heating with carbon.

....

....

[2]

  b) What is the name given to this type of reaction?

....

[1]

  c) Complete the word equation for the reaction of iron oxide with carbon.

iron(III) oxide + ... → .... + ...

[1]

[Total 4 marks]

2 Zinc oxide can be reduced to zinc using carbon.

  a) Write and balance the chemical equation for this reaction.

.... + ... → .... + ...

[2]

  b) Identify the reducing agent in this reaction.

....

[1]

[Total 3 marks]

3 Not all metals can be extracted using carbon.
Some need to be extracted using a different method.

  a) Give the name of the process used to extract these metals.

....

[1]

  b) Explain why not all metals can be extracted using carbon.

....

....

[1]

[Total 2 marks]

Score:

9

Extracting Aluminium

1 Aluminium is extracted from purified aluminium oxide by electrolysis.

positive carbon electrode

‒

carbon lining as negative electrode

aluminium oxide dissolved in molten cryolite

molten aluminium

a) Electrolysis is an expensive process.

   i) What makes this process so expensive?

   ....

   [1]

   ii) How does dissolving aluminium oxide in cryolite help reduce the cost of electrolysis?

   ....

   ....

   [2]

b) A different reaction occurs at each electrode in the electrolysis of aluminium oxide.
   Give the two ionic half-equations that represent these reactions.

   It's really important that you remember these half-equations. You need to balance them correctly to get all of the marks.

   Half-equation 1 ....

   Half-equation 2 ....

   [3]

c) Are aluminium ions oxidised or reduced in this electrolysis reaction?
   Explain your answer.

   ....

   ....

   [2]

d) Another cost associated with the electrolysis of aluminium ore is the replacement of electrodes.
   Which electrode needs to be regularly replaced? Explain why.

   ....

   ....

   [2]

   [Total 10 marks]

   Score:

   10

Extracting Iron

1   Iron can be extracted from its ore in a blast furnace.
     The diagram below shows a section through a blast furnace.

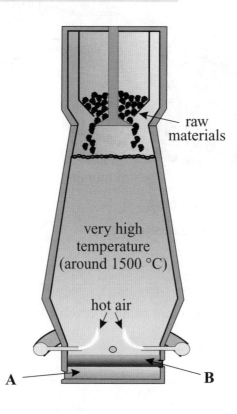

a) i) Name the ore that iron is commonly extracted from.

    ....
                                                                                                                                            [1]

    ii) Name the two other raw materials that are fed into the furnace.

        1 ....

        2 ....
                                                                                                                                            [2]

b) State what labels **A** and **B** show on the diagram above.

    A ....

    B ....
                                                                                                                                            [2]

c) Explain why air is blown into the furnace.

    ....

    ....
                                                                                                                                            [1]

                                                                                                                                  [Total 6 marks]

2 The main stages of the extraction of iron in a blast furnace involve converting iron ore to iron.

a) i) Complete the following chemical equations that show the first two steps in the process.

Step 1:   C + ... → ....

Step 2:   .... + ... → 2CO

[2]

ii) Describe what happens in the blast furnace when these reactions occur.

....

....

....

[2]

b) i) Write a balanced chemical equation to show the production of iron from iron ore using carbon monoxide.

....

[2]

ii) In this reaction is the iron oxide reduced or oxidised?

....

[1]

[Total 7 marks]

3 The final stages of iron extraction involve removing impurities from the iron.

a) Name the main impurity that is present in the iron.   ....

[1]

b) Limestone ($CaCO_3$) is used to remove this impurity.
The limestone is firstly broken down by the heat in the blast furnace.
Write the chemical equation for this reaction.

....

[1]

c) A final reaction produces slag, which can be tapped off from the blast furnace.
Write the chemical equation for this reaction.

....

[1]

[Total 3 marks]

Exam Practice Tip

It's really important that you learn all of the reactions involved in the extraction of iron using a blast furnace. Exam questions on this topic could ask you to write out the equations, and it's also a good idea to know what's going on inside the furnace at the different stages of the process.

Score

☐

16

Uses of Iron and Aluminium

1 Iron and aluminium have similar properties.
For example, they both have high melting points.

a) State **three** other properties that iron and aluminium have in common.

1 ....

2 ....

3 ....

[3]

b) Aluminium is used in the manufacture of aeroplanes.
Suggest why aluminium is more suited to this role than iron.

....

....

[1]

[Total 4 marks]

2 The properties of iron are changed when it is converted into an alloy.

The table below contains information about two different alloys of iron — cast iron and steel.

Alloy	Hardness	Malleability
Cast iron	Very hard	Poor
Steel	Very hard	Very good

The malleability of a metal is how easily it can be hammered into shape without breaking.

a) Suggest which of these alloys is used for the construction of car bodies.
Give a reason for your choice.

Alloy ....

Reason ....

....

[2]

b) Stainless steel is an alloy that is often used to make knives, forks and other kitchen equipment.
Suggest a property of this alloy that makes it well suited for this use.

....

[1]

[Total 3 marks]

Score: ☐

7

😖 ☐   😐 ☐   🙂 ☐

Fractional Distillation of Crude Oil

1 Crude oil can be separated by fractional distillation into several different fractions.

a) Each fraction in crude oil is mostly made of molecules containing only carbon and hydrogen. What name is given to these molecules? ....

[1]

b) Use words from the box to explain how crude oil is separated into different fractions in the fractionating column. Each word may be used once, more than once, or not at all.

gas   lower   down   higher   condense   up   boil   liquid

The crude oil is heated until most of it has turned into ....

The fractionating column has a temperature gradient and so when the substances that make up

crude oil reach a part of the column where the temperature is .... than their

boiling point, they .... and drain off. Different fractions have different boiling

points so they drain off at different points as they move .... the column.

[4]

c) Label the fractionating column below with the names of the different fractions shown in the box.

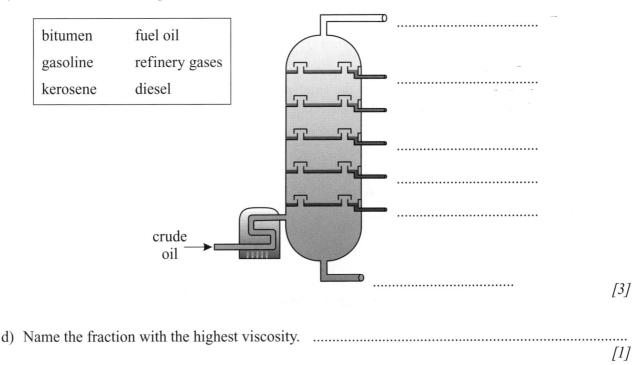

bitumen   fuel oil

gasoline   refinery gases

kerosene   diesel

crude oil →

....

....

....

....

....

....

[3]

d) Name the fraction with the highest viscosity. ....

[1]

e) Describe the link between the size of the molecules in crude oil fractions and their boiling points.

....

[1]

f) State **one** use of fuel oil.

....

[1]

[Total 11 marks]

Score: ☐

11

😟 ☐   😐 ☐   🙂 ☐

Pollutants

1   Fumes from faulty central heating boilers can contain carbon monoxide.

a) What can cause carbon monoxide to be produced when fuel is burnt in a boiler?

....

[1]

b) Explain why carbon monoxide is poisonous.

....

....

[1]

[Total 2 marks]

2   Nitrogen oxides can be produced when fossil fuels are burnt.

a) i) Describe the conditions needed for nitrogen oxides to form.

....

[1]

ii) Give an example of where this reaction might take place.

....

[1]

b) Nitrogen oxides react with moisture in the atmosphere.
    Name the product that is formed when this occurs.

....

[1]

c) Nitrogen oxides contribute to acid rain.

i) Name **one** other gas that contributes to acid rain.

....

[1]

ii) Give **two** effects of acid rain on the environment.

1 ....

....

2 ....

....

[2]

[Total 6 marks]

Score:

8

Cracking Hydrocarbons

1 Cracking alters the molecules obtained in fractional distillation.

a) Why is cracking necessary?

....

....

....

....

[4]

b) The apparatus shown below can be used to crack paraffin in the lab.

i) Identify where the paraffin is within the apparatus.

....

[1]

ii) What is the role of silica?

....

[1]

iii) What collects in the gas jar?

....

[1]

[Total 7 marks]

2 When decane is cracked, octane and ethene can be produced.

a) Write the chemical equation for the cracking of decane to make octane and ethene.

....

[1]

b) Put a cross in the box next to the temperature range this reaction would be carried out at in industry.

☐ 450 °C – 500 °C   ☐ 500 °C – 650 °C   ☐ 600 °C – 700 °C

[1]

[Total 2 marks]

Score: ☐

9

Addition Polymers

1 An addition polymer is made by joining together lots of small molecules.

What is the name given to these repeating small molecules?

....

[Total 1 mark]

2 The equation below shows a polymerisation reaction to form poly(ethene).

$$n \left(\begin{array}{c} H \quad H \\ | \quad\ | \\ C = C \\ | \quad\ | \\ H \quad H \end{array} \right) \longrightarrow \left(\begin{array}{c} H \quad H \\ | \quad\ | \\ C - C \\ | \quad\ | \\ H \quad H \end{array} \right)_n$$

a) What is the name of the monomer used to form poly(ethene)?

....

[1]

b) The polymer poly(propene) can be made by addition polymerisation. The diagram on the right shows the displayed formula for part of a poly(propene) molecule.

$$-\overset{\displaystyle H}{\underset{\displaystyle H}{\overset{|}{\underset{|}{C}}}}-\overset{\displaystyle H}{\underset{\displaystyle CH_3}{\overset{|}{\underset{|}{C}}}}-\overset{\displaystyle H}{\underset{\displaystyle H}{\overset{|}{\underset{|}{C}}}}-\overset{\displaystyle H}{\underset{\displaystyle CH_3}{\overset{|}{\underset{|}{C}}}}-\overset{\displaystyle H}{\underset{\displaystyle H}{\overset{|}{\underset{|}{C}}}}-\overset{\displaystyle H}{\underset{\displaystyle CH_3}{\overset{|}{\underset{|}{C}}}}-\overset{\displaystyle H}{\underset{\displaystyle H}{\overset{|}{\underset{|}{C}}}}-\overset{\displaystyle H}{\underset{\displaystyle CH_3}{\overset{|}{\underset{|}{C}}}}-$$

   i) Draw the structure of the monomer that is used to make poly(propene).

[1]

   ii) Give the name of the monomer used to make poly(propene).

....

[1]

[Total 3 marks]

3 The diagram below shows the monomer that makes up poly(chloroethene) (PVC). | PAPER 2 |

$$\overset{H}{\underset{H}{\diagdown}} C = C \overset{\diagup Cl}{\underset{\diagdown H}{}}$$

Draw the repeat unit for PVC.

[Total 1 mark]   Score: ☐

5

☹ ☐   ☺ ☐   ☺ ☐

More on Polymers and Their Uses

1   Different polymers have different properties, which makes them suitable for particular uses.

a) State one use of poly(ethene).

    ....
    [1]

b) Poly(propene) is resistant to heat. Give a use of this polymer that is linked to this property.

    ....
    [1]

c) Pipes can be made from poly(chloroethene). Give another use of this polymer. | PAPER 2 |

    ....
    [1]

    [Total 3 marks]

2   Most addition polymers are difficult to dispose of, so it's good for the environment to reuse them as many times as possible.

    Explain why addition polymers are difficult to dispose of.

    ....

    ....
    [Total 2 marks]

3   Many polymers are formed by addition polymerisation. | PAPER 2 |
     The polymer nylon is formed by a different process.

a) What is the name of this process?

    ....
    [1]

b) The equation below shows two monomers joining together during the formation of nylon.

$$\begin{array}{c} O \quad\; H \quad O \\ \| \quad\;\; | \quad\; \| \\ C - C - C \\ | \quad\; | \quad\; | \\ OH \; H \quad OH \end{array} \;+\; \begin{array}{c} H \quad H \quad H \\ | \quad\; | \quad\; | \\ N - C - N \\ | \quad\; | \quad\; | \\ H \quad H \quad H \end{array} \longrightarrow \begin{array}{c} O \quad\; H \quad O \quad\quad H \quad H \quad H \\ \| \quad\;\; | \quad\; \| \quad\quad | \quad\; | \quad\; | \\ C - C - C \,-\, N - C - N \\ | \quad\; | \quad\quad\quad\quad\; | \quad\; | \\ OH \; H \quad\quad\quad\quad H \quad H \end{array} \;+\; ?$$

    Name the second product of the reaction and give its chemical formula.

    Name ....   Chemical formula ....
    [2]

    [Total 3 marks]

    Score: ☐

    8

😦 ☐   😐 ☐   🙂 ☐

Section 5 — Chemistry in Industry

The Haber Process

1   The Haber process is used to make ammonia, which is widely used in industry.

a) Complete the chemical equation for the reaction.

.... + ... $\rightleftharpoons$ $2NH_3$

[2]

b) State the name of the two reactants in the forward reaction and a source of each one.

Reactant 1: .... Source: ....

Reactant 2: .... Source: ....

[4]

c) Name **two** things that are manufactured using ammonia.

1 ....

2 ....

[2]

[Total 8 marks]

2   The Haber process is carried out under a specific set of conditions.

a) Identify the industrial conditions used in the production of ammonia from the boxes below.

Temperature	200 °C	350 °C	450 °C	800 °C	1000 °C
Pressure	200 atm	300 atm	450 atm	700 atm	1000 atm

The unit of atmospheres can be shortened to atm.

Temperature used: .... °C

Pressure used: .... atm

[2]

b) Name the catalyst used in the Haber process.

....

[1]

c) In the Haber process, gases pass through a reaction chamber before entering a cooling chamber.

Explain how cooling the gases allows ammonia to be separated from
unused hydrogen and nitrogen, and state what happens to these unused gases.

....

....

....

[3]

[Total 6 marks]

Score: [   ]

14

The Contact Process

1   The contact process is used to manufacture sulfuric acid.

Complete the table below with the conditions used in the contact process.

Temperature	....
Pressure	....
Catalyst	....

[Total 3 marks]

2   The contact process involves several different reactions.

Complete and balance the following equations involved in the contact process, and briefly describe each step of the process.

a)   Step 1:

Equation   .... + ... $\longrightarrow$ SO_2

Description ....
....

[2]

b)   Step 2:

Equation   .... + ... $\rightleftharpoons$ .....SO_3

Description ....
....

[3]

c)   Step 3:

Equation SO_3 + ... $\longrightarrow$ ....

Description ....
....

[2]

d)   Step 4:

Equation   .... + ... $\longrightarrow$ .....H_2SO_4

Description ....
....

[3]

[Total 10 marks]

3   Sulfuric acid has lots of different uses in industry.

Give **three** uses of sulfuric acid made in the contact process.

1 ....

2 ....

3 ....

[Total 3 marks]

Score:

16

Electrolysis of Brine

1 The electrolysis of brine is carried out on a large scale industrially.

a) The process uses concentrated brine. What is brine a solution of?

....

[1]

b) The diagram below shows a diaphragm cell used for the electrolysis of brine.

Name the products of this reaction and identify which location on the diagram, **A** or **B**, they are collected from.

Product 1 .... collected at ....

Product 2 .... collected at ....

[4]

c) Different reactions take place at each of the electrodes in the diaphragm cell.

i) Write a half-equation for the reaction at the negative electrode, and describe what happens during the reaction.

Don't forget to balance half-equations.

Half-equation ....

What happens ....

[3]

ii) Write a half-equation for the reaction at the positive electrode, and describe what happens during the reaction.

Half-equation ....

What happens ....

[3]

[Total 11 marks]

2   The electrolysis of brine generates products that can be used in industry for the manufacture of a variety of different chemicals and household goods.

A company carries out large-scale electrolysis of brine.
The table below shows the final uses of the electrolysis products the company sells.

Final use	Percentage of company's electrolysis output used for this purpose
hydrochloric acid	29%
margarine	19%
soap	?
other	35%

a) What percentage of the company's output is used for the manufacture of soap?

    ....
                                                                                                      [1]

b) State the product of brine electrolysis that is used in the manufacture of the following products.

    i) hydrochloric acid:

        ....

    ii) paper pulp:

        ....

    iii) soap:

        ....
                                                                                                      [3]

c) Which **two** products of brine electrolysis can be used in the manufacture of bleach?

    1 ....

    2 ....
                                                                                                      [2]

d) Name the product of brine electrolysis that can be used in the sterilisation of water supplies.

    ....
                                                                                                      [1]
                                                                                          [Total 7 marks]

Exam Practice Tip

In this topic it's important that you remember the products of brine electrolysis and what they can be used for. It's good to know the half-equations really well too because they describe what's happening inside the diaphragm cell — and don't forget they need to be balanced.

Score

18

Candidate Surname	Candidate Forename(s)

Centre Number	Candidate Number

Certificate
International GCSE

Chemistry
Paper 1C

Practice Paper
Time allowed: 2 hours

You must have:
- A ruler.
- A calculator.

Total marks:

Instructions to candidates
- Use **black** ink to write your answers.
- Write your name and other details in the spaces provided above.
- Answer **all** questions in the spaces provided.
- In calculations, show clearly how you worked out your answers.
- You will need to answer some questions by placing a cross in a box, like this: ☒
  To change your answer, draw a line through the box like this: ☒
  Then mark your new answer as normal.

Information for candidates
- The marks available are given in brackets at the end of each question.
- There are 120 marks available for this paper.
- You might find the periodic table on the inside of the front cover useful.

Advice for candidates
- Read all the questions carefully.
- Write your answers as clearly and neatly as possible.
- Keep in mind how much time you have left.

Get the answers

Your free Online Edition of this book includes the complete answers for this Exam Paper — you can even print them out. There's more info about how to get your Online Edition at the front of this book.

Answer **all** questions

1   Atoms contain protons, neutrons and electrons.

(a)   Complete the table to show the relative charges and relative masses of protons, neutrons and electrons.

[2]

Particle	Mass	Charge
Proton	1	+1
Neutron	....	....
Electron	....	....

(b)   The table below shows the numbers of protons, neutrons and electrons in six different atoms.

Atom	Number of protons	Number of neutrons	Number of electrons
A	5	6	5
B	7	7	7
C	6	8	6
D	6	6	6
E	10	10	10
F	4	5	4

Which **two** atoms are isotopes of the same element? Explain your answer.

Atoms .... and ....

Explanation ....

....

[2]

Turn over ▶

Zinc appears in the periodic table as shown below.

65

Zn

Zinc

30

(c)   How many protons, neutrons and electrons are there in an atom of zinc?

Protons ....   Neutrons ....   Electrons ....

[3]

(d)   Zinc sulfate is a compound with the formula $ZnSO_4$.

(i)   What is a compound?

....

....

[2]

(ii)   Calculate the relative formula mass of zinc sulfate.

....

[2]

[Total 11 marks]

2 Nitrogen dioxide is an atmospheric pollutant.

(a) Suggest why nitrogen dioxide levels can be particularly high in cities.

....

....

....

....
[2]

(b) Nitrogen dioxide can react with water in the atmosphere to form nitric acid, which falls as acid rain. Acid rain can damage buildings made from limestone, which is mainly calcium carbonate.

(i) Complete the word equation for the reaction between nitric acid and calcium carbonate.

nitric acid + calcium carbonate →

.... + ... + ...
[2]

(ii) Name **one** other gas that can cause acid rain.

....
[1]

(iii) Give **one** problem, other than damage to buildings, caused by acid rain.

....
[1]

[Total 6 marks]

Turn over ▶

3 The halogens make up Group 7 of the periodic table.
The table below shows some of the physical properties of the first four halogens.

Halogen	Atomic number	Melting Point (°C)	Boiling Point (°C)	Colour at room temperature
Fluorine	9	−220	−188	very pale yellow
Chlorine	17		−34	green
Bromine	35	−7	59	
Iodine	53	114	185	dark grey

(a) (i) Predict the melting point of chlorine, using the data in the table.
Place a cross (x) in the appropriate box to indicate your answer.

☐ −231 °C

☐ −216 °C

☐ −101 °C

☐ 107 °C

[1]

(ii) Explain your answer to part i)

....

....

[1]

(b) Describe the appearance of bromine at room temperature.

....

[2]

(c) Write down the balanced symbol equation for the reaction between bromine and potassium iodide.

....

[2]

(d) (i) Complete the diagram below to show the electronic structure of a chlorine atom.
Mark each electron using an 'X'.

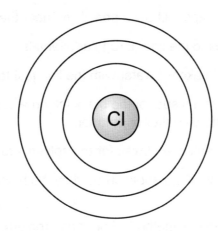

[1]

(ii) Explain how the group number of chlorine in the periodic table is related to its electronic structure.

....

....

....

[2]

(e) Chlorine is bubbled through sodium iodide solution. What will happen?
Explain your answer in terms of the relative positions of chlorine and iodine in the periodic table.

....

....

....

....

....

[3]

(f) Chlorine can combine with hydrogen to form hydrogen chloride.
Explain why hydrogen chloride forms an acidic solution in water.

....

....

....

[2]

[Total 14 marks]

Turn over ▶

Practice Paper 1C

4   A student wanted to find out which of five dyes could be present in a particular black ink.

(a)   The student was asked to suggest a method. This is the method the student suggested:

- Take a piece of filter paper. Draw a pencil line near the bottom.

- Add spots of the dyes to the line at regular intervals.

- Put the paper into a beaker of water with the line just touching the water.

- Repeat these steps with a spot of the black ink on a second piece of filter paper, and put this paper into a beaker of ethanol.

- Place a lid on each beaker, and wait for the solvents to travel to the top of the paper.

- Compare the positions of the spots created by the black ink with those created by the dyes.

Identify **two** problems with this method. For each problem, suggest how you would alter the method to carry out the experiment correctly.

You can assume the student takes sensible safety precautions.

Problem 1 ....

....

....

Correction ....

....

....

....

Problem 2 ....

....

....

Correction ....

....

....

....

....

[4]

(b)   The student repeated the experiment using the correct method.
The results are shown below.

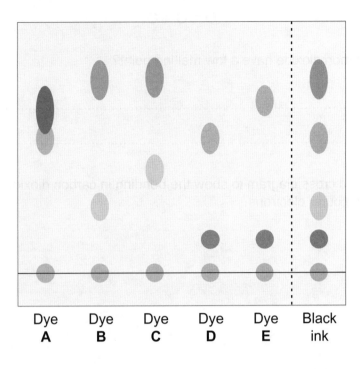

| Dye A | Dye B | Dye C | Dye D | Dye E | Black ink |

Which dyes (**A-E**) could have been present in the black ink? Explain your answer.

Dyes ....

Explanation ....

....

....

....

[2]

[Total 6 marks]

5   Carbon dioxide is a simple molecule whose displayed formula is shown below.

$$O=C=O$$

(a)   Why does carbon dioxide have a low melting point?

....

....
                                                                                                    [1]

(b)   Draw a dot and cross diagram to show the bonding in carbon dioxide.
       Only show the outer electrons.

                                                                                                    [2]

(c)   Explain how the properties of carbon dioxide make it useful for extinguishing fires.

....

....

....
                                                                                                    [2]

(d)   Another compound containing carbon is made up of 96.0 g of calcium, 28.8 g of carbon
       and 115.2 g of oxygen.
       Calculate the empirical formula of the compound.

                                                     Empirical formula = ...
                                                                                                    [3]

(e) Carbon dioxide can be produced by heating zinc carbonate ($ZnCO_3$).
Zinc oxide (ZnO) is left behind.

    (i) State the name for this type of reaction.

....

[1]

    (ii) Suggest how you could collect the carbon dioxide produced in this experiment.

....

....

[1]

(f) Which of the following sentences correctly describes the solubility of carbon dioxide
in water? Place a cross (x) in the appropriate box to indicate your answer.

☐ Carbon dioxide is insoluble in water, but becomes soluble under pressure.

☐ Carbon dioxide is slightly soluble in water, but becomes less soluble under pressure.

☐ Carbon dioxide is slightly soluble in water, but becomes more soluble under pressure.

☐ Carbon dioxide is very soluble in water, but becomes less soluble under pressure.

[1]

(g) Carbon dioxide is a greenhouse gas.

    (i) What is meant by the term **greenhouse gas**?

....

....

....

[2]

    (ii) What percentage of the air is made up of carbon dioxide?

....

[1]

    (iii) Give **one** possible effect of increasing the amount of carbon dioxide in the atmosphere.

....

....

[1]

[Total 15 marks]

Turn over ▶

98

6 Analytical tests can be used to identify different substances.

(a) Suggest tests that could be used to distinguish between the following pairs of compounds in solution. You should describe the tests and the results expected for each solution.

[4]

Solution A	Solution B	Description of test	Observations	
			Solution A	Solution B
iron(II) chloride	iron(III) chloride			
sodium chloride	sodium iodide			

(b) When an unknown compound is placed in a blue Bunsen flame, it gives a yellow-orange colour. If dilute acid is added to the compound, a gas is produced. When this gas is bubbled through limewater, the limewater goes cloudy.

Identify the compound by its chemical name.

....

[2]

[Total 6 marks]

7   The displayed formulae of two gases are shown below.

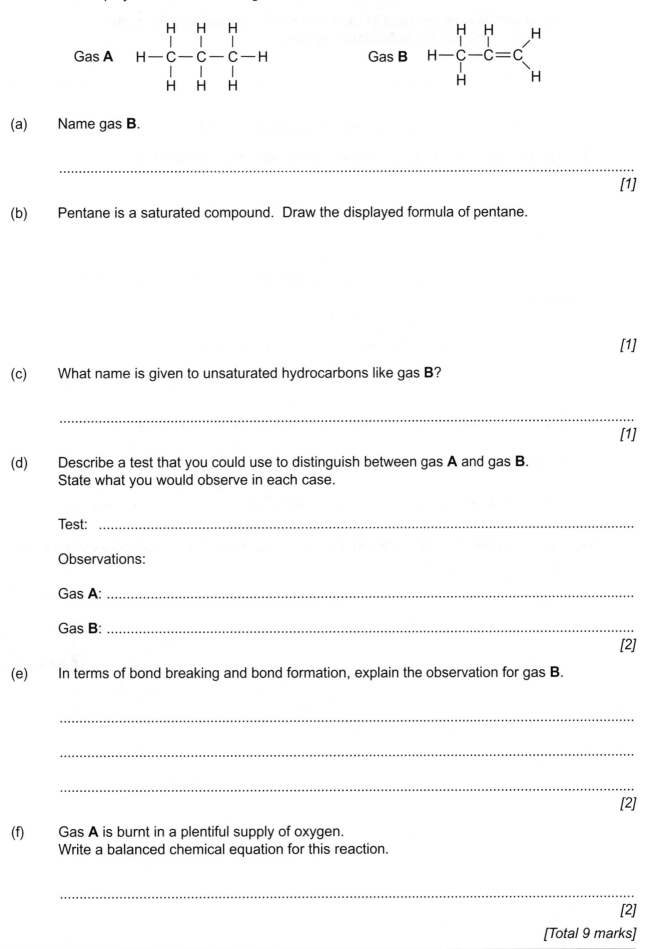

(a)   Name gas **B**.

        ....
        [1]

(b)   Pentane is a saturated compound. Draw the displayed formula of pentane.

        [1]

(c)   What name is given to unsaturated hydrocarbons like gas **B**?

        ....
        [1]

(d)   Describe a test that you could use to distinguish between gas **A** and gas **B**.
        State what you would observe in each case.

        Test: ....

        Observations:

        Gas **A**: ....

        Gas **B**: ....
        [2]

(e)   In terms of bond breaking and bond formation, explain the observation for gas **B**.

        ....

        ....

        ....
        [2]

(f)   Gas **A** is burnt in a plentiful supply of oxygen.
        Write a balanced chemical equation for this reaction.

        ....
        [2]
        [Total 9 marks]

8 Metals can be extracted from their oxides using several different methods.

(a) Copper can be extracted from its oxide in a reduction reaction using carbon.
State what is meant by a **reduction reaction**.

....
                                                                                                    [1]

(b) Aluminium is extracted from aluminium oxide by electrolysis.

(i) Explain why aluminium cannot be extracted by reduction with carbon.

....

....
                                                                                                    [1]

(ii) The aluminium oxide is dissolved in molten cryolite for the electrolysis reaction.
Explain why.

....

....
                                                                                                    [2]

(iii) Write the half-equations for the reactions that occur at each electrode.

Negative electrode ....

Positive electrode ....
                                                                                                    [4]

(iv) The positive electrode is made from carbon. Explain why it has to be regularly replaced.

....

....
                                                                                                    [1]
                                                                                          [Total 9 marks]

9   Self-heating cans use exothermic chemical reactions to heat up their contents.
     When a seal is broken two chemicals mix and react, heating up the can.
     Calcium oxide and water can be used to heat up drinks in this way.

(a)   What is an exothermic reaction?

       ....

       ....
                                                                                              [1]

(b)   A student wanted to test the reaction of different substances with water
       to see if they could be used to cool drinks down.

       Outline an experiment the student could carry out to test different substances.

       ....

       ....

       ....

       ....

       ....
                                                                                              [3]

(c)   Calcium oxide (CaO) is produced when iron(III) oxide (Fe_2O_3) reacts with calcium.
       Iron is also produced. Write a balanced chemical equation for this reaction.

       ....
                                                                                              [2]
                                                                              [Total 6 marks]

Turn over ▶

10 The graph shows the volume of gas produced over time when lumps of zinc are reacted with dilute sulfuric acid.

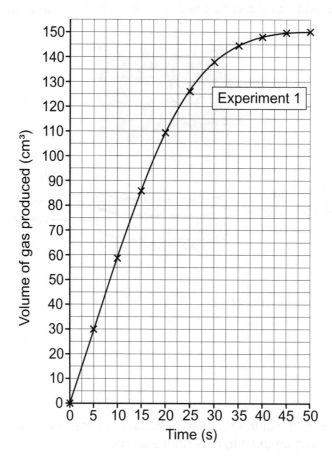

In a second experiment, some copper sulfate catalyst was added to the acid.
The same amount of zinc was used as before, and the lumps were of a similar size.
The same volume of dilute sulfuric acid was also used.
The results are shown in the table.

Time (secs)	Volume of gas formed (cm³)
	Experiment 2
0	0
5	50
10	100
15	130
20	143
25	148
30	150
35	150
40	150
45	150
50	150

(a) Plot the results of the second experiment on the graph above.

Draw a curve of best fit through the points. Label the line 'Experiment 2'.

[2]

(b)   How long does it take to form half of the total amount of gas collected
        in the second experiment?

        ....
                                                                                                                            [1]

(c)   What do the curves show about how the rate of reaction changes as
        the reaction proceeds?

        ....
                                                                                                                            [1]

(d)   State how the catalyst affects the reaction rate and explain how you can tell this from
        the graph.

        ....

        ....

        ....
                                                                                                                            [1]

(e)   Explain, in terms of activation energy, how catalysts affect reaction rates.

        ....

        ....

        ....
                                                                                                                            [1]
                                                                                                            [Total 6 marks]

Turn over ▶

11 Titration with 0.050 mol/dm³ sulfuric acid was used to determine the concentration of calcium hydroxide solution. In the titration, 8.80 cm³ of sulfuric acid were needed to neutralise 10.0 cm³ of the calcium hydroxide solution.

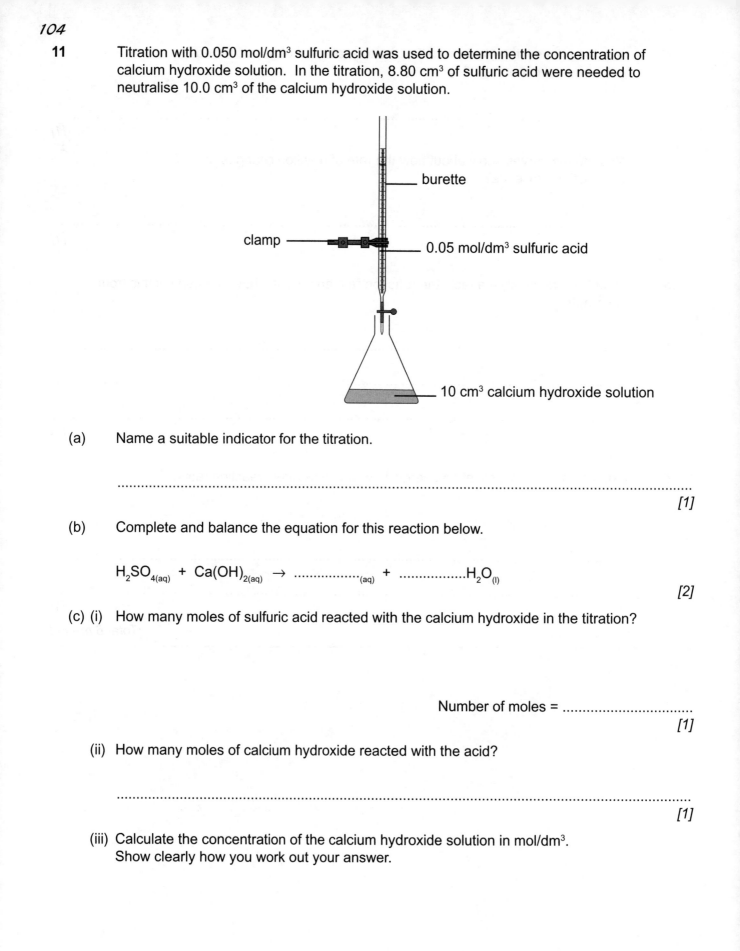

(a) Name a suitable indicator for the titration.

....

[1]

(b) Complete and balance the equation for this reaction below.

$H_2SO_{4(aq)}$ + $Ca(OH)_{2(aq)}$ → ....$_{(aq)}$ + ...$H_2O_{(l)}$

[2]

(c) (i) How many moles of sulfuric acid reacted with the calcium hydroxide in the titration?

Number of moles = ...

[1]

(ii) How many moles of calcium hydroxide reacted with the acid?

....

[1]

(iii) Calculate the concentration of the calcium hydroxide solution in mol/dm³.
      Show clearly how you work out your answer.

Concentration = ... mol/dm³

[1]

(iv) Calculate the concentration of the calcium hydroxide solution in g/dm³.
The M$_r$ for calcium hydroxide is 74.

Show clearly how you work out your answer.

Concentration = ... g/dm³

[1]

(d)   The pH curve below shows the change in pH that occurred during a second titration where sodium hydroxide was being added to a weak acid.

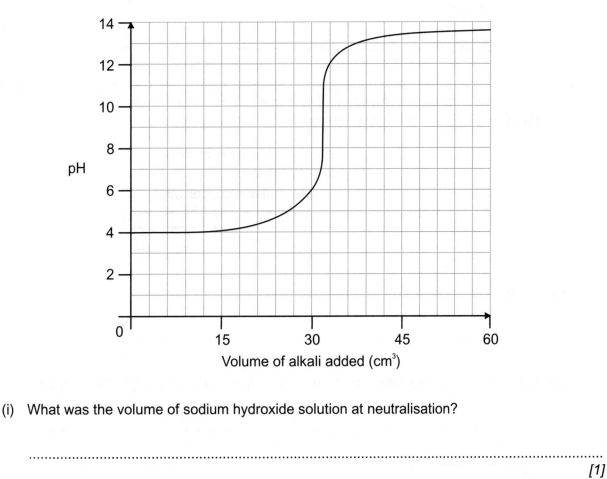

Volume of alkali added (cm³)

(i)   What was the volume of sodium hydroxide solution at neutralisation?

....

[1]

(ii) What was the pH of the solution when 46.0 cm³ of sodium hydroxide was added?

....

[1]

[Total 9 marks]

Turn over ▶

Practice Paper 1C

12   Iron pipes need protection from rusting.

(a)   What conditions cause iron to rust?

....

....
               [2]

(b)   Rusting is a type of corrosion. What causes corrosion?
          Place a cross (x) in the appropriate box to indicate your answer.

     ☐   distillation

     ☐   electrolysis

     ☐   oxidation

     ☐   reduction
               [1]

(c)   Paint can be used to stop underground iron pipes rusting, but they will eventually need repainting or replacing. An alternative to this is to connect a large piece of magnesium to the pipe, as shown in the diagram below.

          ▭ —Magnesium block

          — Insulated copper wire

          `Iron pipe

(i)   What name is given to this kind of corrosion protection?

....
               [1]

(ii)   Explain why the magnesium protects the iron from rusting, and how this happens.

....

....

....
               [2]

(d)   A coat of zinc could be applied to the iron pipes to prevent them rusting.
          What name is given to this method of corrosion protection?

....
               [1]

              [Total 7 marks]

13   The balanced equation below shows what happens when a strip of magnesium metal is dissolved in a solution of hydrochloric acid.

$$Mg_{(s)} + 2HCl_{(aq)} \rightarrow MgCl_{2(aq)} + H_{2(g)}$$

(a)   A student dissolved a piece of magnesium in an excess of hydrochloric acid.
7.50 g of $MgCl_2$ was produced. What mass of magnesium did the student start with?

Mass of magnesium = ... g

[3]

(b)   Describe how the student could test for the gas produced in this reaction, and state what he would observe.

Test ....

....

Observation ....

....

[2]

[Total 5 marks]

14 Soluble salts can be made by reacting an acid with an insoluble base or an alkali.

(a) An excess of zinc oxide is added to a beaker of dilute hydrochloric acid.
The mixture is stirred and the acid is neutralised.

dilute hydrochloric acid

excess of zinc oxide

(i) How could you tell when all the acid has been neutralised?

....
[1]

(ii) Give the products of this reaction.

....
[2]

(b) Describe how you could obtain a pure, dry sample of calcium chloride
from the alkali calcium hydroxide and dilute hydrochloric acid.

....

....

....

....

....

....
[3]

(c)   Which **two** substances from the list below could be mixed to obtain calcium sulfate by precipitation? Write the letters of the substances.

A $BaSO_4$

B $CaCl_2$

C $CaCO_3$

D H_2SO_4

Substances .... and ....

[2]

(d)   Complete and balance the chemical equation for the reaction between hydrochloric acid and copper carbonate. Include state symbols.

$CuCO_3$(.......) + ... $\rightarrow$ ....

[3]

[Total 11 marks]

[Total for paper 120 marks]

Candidate Surname		Candidate Forename(s)	

Centre Number	Candidate Number

Certificate
International GCSE

Chemistry
Paper 2C

Practice Paper
Time allowed: 1 hour

You must have:
• A ruler.
• A calculator.

Total marks:

Instructions to candidates
• Use **black** ink to write your answers.
• Write your name and other details in the spaces provided above.
• Answer **all** questions in the spaces provided.
• In calculations, show clearly how you worked out your answers.

Information for candidates
• The marks available are given in brackets at the end of each question.
• There are 60 marks available for this paper.
• You might find the periodic table on the inside of the front cover useful.

Advice for candidates
• Read all the questions carefully.
• Write your answers as clearly and neatly as possible.
• Keep in mind how much time you have left.

Get the answers
Your free Online Edition of this book includes the complete answers for this Exam Paper — you can even print them out. There's more info about how to get your Online Edition at the front of this book.

Answer **all** questions

1   The diagram shows the electronic structures of a sodium atom and a chlorine atom.

(a)   Chlorine has two major isotopes, ^{35}Cl and ^{37}Cl.

(i)   State what is meant by the term **isotope**.

....

....

                                                                                                        [1]

(ii) ^{35}Cl has a relative abundance of 25%.

The relative atomic mass of chlorine is 35.5. Show how this value is calculated.

....

....

                                                                                                        [2]

(b)   Sodium and chlorine react to form the ionic compound sodium chloride.

Draw a dot and cross diagram of sodium chloride. Show only the outer electrons.

                                                                                                        [3]

Turn over ▶

Practice Paper 2C

(c)   Draw a diagram to show the structure of the ions in a crystal of sodium chloride. Include at least four ions of each element in the diagram.

[1]

(d)   Explain why sodium chloride has a high melting point.

....

....

....

[2]

[Total 9 marks]

2 The Haber process is used to make ammonia from nitrogen and hydrogen.
The chemical equation for the reaction is:

$$N_{2(g)} + 3H_{2(g)} \rightleftharpoons 2NH_{3(g)}$$

(a) The Haber process reaction reaches a dynamic equilibrium. What does this mean?

....

....

[1]

(b) Give the temperature at which the Haber process is carried out.

....

[1]

(c) The reaction between nitrogen and hydrogen is exothermic.

Explain what will happen to the yield of ammonia if the temperature is increased.

....

....

....

[2]

(d) Give the pressure at which the Haber process is carried out.

....

[1]

(e) Explain what will happen to the yield of ammonia if the pressure is decreased.

....

....

....

[2]

(f) What catalyst is used in the Haber process?

....

[1]

Turn over ▶

(g)   In part of a Haber process reaction vessel, the reaction mixture is cooled to around 30 °C.
        What does this cooling enable?

        ....

        ....

        ....

        [2]

(h)   Give **two** uses of the ammonia produced in the Haber process.

        Use 1 ....

        Use 2 ....

        [2]

        [Total 12 marks]

3   A student investigates the reactions of the Group 1 metals lithium, sodium and potassium, with water. The student's observations are recorded in the table below.

Metal	Observations
lithium	Fizzes, moves across the surface
sodium	Fizzes strongly, melts into a round ball, moves across the surface
potassium	Fizzes violently, melts into a round ball, moves across the surface, a flame is seen

The student decides that the order of reactivity of the three metals is:

- potassium (most reactive)

- sodium

- lithium (least reactive)

(a)   Give **two** pieces of evidence from the table that support the student's conclusion.

1...

....

2...

....

[2]

(b)   Explain the pattern of reactivity that the student has noticed.

....

....

....

....

[2]

(c)   Write a balanced chemical equation for the reaction between lithium and water.

....

[2]

Turn over ▶

116

(d)   The student accidentally mixes up some unlabelled samples of lithium chloride and
        potassium chloride. The student decides to do a test to find out which is which,
        using a moistened wire loop. Briefly describe the test that the student could carry out,
        and what the results would be.

....

....

....

[2]

[Total 8 marks]

4   Hydrogen can be burned in oxygen and used as a fuel.

$$2H_2 + O_2 \rightarrow 2H_2O$$

(a)   Calculate the enthalpy change for the reaction. The bond energy values are given below.

Bond energy values (kJ/mol):

O=O   +498

H–H   +436

O–H   +464

Enthalpy change = ... kJ/mol

[4]

(b)   Is bond breaking an exothermic or endothermic process?

....

[1]

[Total 5 marks]

5   A student is investigating how the rate of the reaction between magnesium strips and hydrochloric acid is affected by the concentration of the acid. The student compares different concentrations of acid by measuring how long it takes for the reaction to produce 20 cm³ of hydrogen gas.

The results of the experiment are shown below.

Concentration of acid (mol/dm³)	Time (s)
0.2	58
0.4	29
0.6	18
0.8	15
1.0	12

(a)   Plot the results on the axes below and draw a line of best fit.

[2]

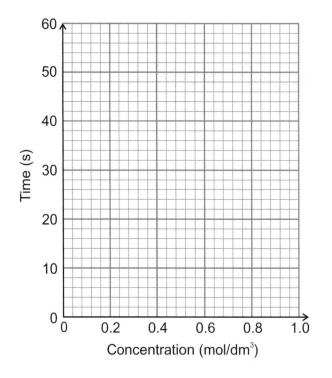

(b)   Use your graph to predict the time that it would take for 20 cm³ of hydrogen gas to form with 0.5 mol/dm³ hydrochloric acid.

 s

[1]

(c)   How could the student make his results more reliable?

....

[1]

(d)   What does the graph show about the effect of concentration on the rate of reaction?

....

....

[1]

(e)   Explain, in terms of collision theory, why concentration affects the rate of a reaction.

....

....

....

....

[2]

(f)   The student carries out the experiment again using 0.6 mol/dm³ hydrochloric acid.
        This time, magnesium powder is used rather than strips of metal.

        The student says "it will take longer than 18 seconds for 20 cm³ of hydrogen gas to form".

        Is the student's prediction correct? Explain your answer.

....

....

....

....

....

[3]

[Total 10 marks]

Turn over ▶

6   The diagram shows the repeat unit of an addition polymer.

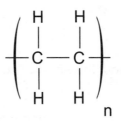

(a)   Draw the displayed formula of the monomer used to make this compound.

[1]

(b)   Explain why addition polymers are generally hard to dispose of.

....

....

[1]

(c)   Complete the table below by giving a use for each addition polymer.

[3]

Polymer	Use
poly(ethene)	....
poly(propene)	....
poly(chloroethene)	....

(d)   Some polymers, such as nylon, are not formed by addition polymerisation.

   (i) State the type of polymerisation used to form nylon.

....

[1]

   (ii) What is produced along with the polymer during this type of polymerisation reaction?

....

[1]

[Total 7 marks]

7   A student is doing an experiment to investigate the electrolysis of sodium chloride solution.

electrodes

sodium chloride (NaCl) solution

(a)   Explain why the sodium chloride has to be in solution for electrolysis to occur.

....

....

[2]

(b)   Complete the half-equation for the reaction occurring at the positive electrode.

positive electrode   .... Cl^- → Cl_2 + ...

[1]

(c)   Why is sodium not formed at the negative electrode?

....

....

[1]

(d)   What useful product remains in solution?

....

[1]

(e)   The student carries out the electrolysis using a current of 4 amps.
Calculate the mass of hydrogen the student would expect to produce after 20 minutes.
(1 faraday = 96000 coulombs.)

The half equation for the reaction at the negative electrode is: $2H^+ + 2e^- → H_2$

Mass of hydrogen = ... g

[4]

[Total 9 marks]

[Total for paper 60 marks]

Answers

Section 1 — Principles of Chemistry

Page 3: States of Matter

1 a) strong *[1 mark]*, regular *[1 mark]*, move *[1 mark]*, hotter *[1 mark]*.
  b) E.g. the particles gain energy *[1 mark]*, move around faster *[1 mark]* and go from being close together to being far apart *[1 mark]*.
2 a) D *[1 mark]*
  b) evaporation *[1 mark]*
  c) The particles gain energy *[1 mark]* and vibrate more *[1 mark]*. This weakens the forces that hold the solid together and makes the solid expand *[1 mark]*. At the point of melting, many of the particles have enough energy to break free from their positions *[1 mark]*.

Page 4: Movement of Particles

1 a) diffusion *[1 mark]*
  b) The water got less purple as the potassium manganate(VII) particles spread further apart *[1 mark]*.
  c) The particles of ammonia are smaller and lighter, so they diffused more quickly *[1 mark]*.
2 Both jars will be the same pale brown colour *[1 mark]* because the random motion of the bromine and air particles means that they will eventually be equally mixed throughout both jars *[1 mark]*.

Page 5: Atoms

1 a) Protons 9, Neutrons 10, Electrons 9
  [1 mark for two correct, 2 marks for all three correct.]
  b)

Particle	Relative mass	Charge
Proton	1	+1
Neutron	1	0
Electron	1/2000	−1

  [1 mark for each correct answer]
An electron's mass is tiny — you'd also get a mark for saying 'negligible'.
  c) a molecule *[1 mark]*
2 a) Atomic number 2, Mass number 4 *[1 mark for both correct]*
  b) the nucleus *[1 mark]*
  c) E.g.

  [1 mark for the electrons, 1 mark for the neutrons, 1 mark for the protons.]

Page 6: Elements, Compounds and Mixtures

1 E.g. elements consist of one type of atom only *[1 mark]*, but compounds are made of two or more different elements which are chemically bonded together *[1 mark]*.

2 a)

Property	Substance
Consists of one type of atom only.	aluminium
Contains different chemicals which can be separated using physical methods.	solid fuel
Made of two or more different elements which are chemically bonded.	aluminium perchlorate

  [1 mark for each correct answer]
  b) i) element *[1 mark]*
   ii) compound *[1 mark]*

Pages 7-8: Separating Mixtures

1 a) E.g. draw a pencil line near the bottom of a sheet of filter paper and add spots of different inks to the line at intervals. *[1 mark]*. Put the paper in a beaker of solvent, e.g. water *[1 mark]*, so that the pencil line and the spots of ink are above the solvent *[1 mark]*.
  b) Printers 1 and 3 could not have produced the document. *[1 mark for both correct]*
2 a) E.g. mix the lawn sand with water to dissolve the ammonium sulfate *[1 mark]*. Filter the mixture using filter paper to remove the sharp sand *[1 mark]*. Pour the remaining solution into an evaporating dish and slowly heat it to evaporate the water *[1 mark]*. Dry the products in a drying oven/desiccator *[1 mark]*.
  b) E.g. the products were not completely dry *[1 mark]*.
3 a) The boiling points of water and methanoic acid are too close together to allow them to be separated by simple distillation *[1 mark]*.
  b)

Temperature on thermometer	Contents of the flask	Contents of the beaker
30 °C	both liquids	no liquid
65 °C	water	propanone
110 °C	no liquid	both liquids

  [3 marks available — 1 mark for each correct row.]
  c) The different liquids in the mixture will all have different boiling points *[1 mark]*. When the mixture is heated, the liquid with the lowest boiling point will evaporate first and it will reach the top of the fractionating column when the temperature there matches its boiling point *[1 mark]*. It can then be condensed and collected *[1 mark]*. When the first liquid has been collected, the temperature can be raised until the next liquid evaporates and reaches the top of the column, and so on *[1 mark]*.
4 brown seaweed *[1 mark]*

Pages 9-10: The Periodic Table and Electron Shells

1 a) By atomic number *[1 mark]*
  b) The number of electrons in the outer shell is the same as the group number *[1 mark]*.
2 a) F *[1 mark]*
  b) Kr *[1 mark]*
  c) S *[1 mark]*
  d) K *[1 mark]*
3 a) 2, 2 *[1 mark]*
  b)

  [1 mark for the 3rd level correct, 1 mark for the 4th level correct.]
The important thing here is not where you place the electrons on each energy level ring, but that the number on each level is correct — fill from the inside outward, and remember that you can never have more than two electrons in the first shell, or more than eight in the others.
  c) 2 *[1 mark]*
4 a) potassium *[1 mark]*
  b) i) It only contains one electron — the first level should have two before the next level is filled *[1 mark]*.
   ii) It contains nine electrons — only eight electrons can fit into the second electron shell *[1 mark]*.

Pages 11-12: Ionic Bonding

1 a) Each magnesium atom loses two electrons *[1 mark]* — oxidation *[1 mark]*.

b) Sulfur atoms have six electrons in their outer shell, so they need two more to make a complete shell of eight electrons *[1 mark]*. Chlorine atoms have seven electrons in their outer shell, so they need one more electron to make a full shell of eight electrons *[1 mark]*.

2 a) i) electrostatic attraction *[1 mark]*, strong *[1 mark]*
   ii) K^+ *[1 mark]*
   iii) Cl^- *[1 mark]*

The last number in the electronic configuration tells you what group the element is in, and therefore how many electrons in its outer shell. Group 1 and 2 elements form positive ions as they lose electrons to leave a full outer shell. Group 6 and 7 elements form negative ions as they need to gain electrons to fill their outer shell.

b) Both nitrate and bromide ions are negatively charged *[1 mark]*. Ionic compounds can only be formed between negative and positive ions *[1 mark]*.

3 a) Al^{3+} *[1 mark]*
   b) Reduction occurs when an atom gains electrons *[1 mark]*.
   c) O^{2-} *[1 mark]*
   d) A *[1 mark]*

4

Element	Electronic configuration	Formula of ion formed
Lithium	2, 1	Li^+
Calcium	2, 8, 8, 2	Ca^{2+}
Sodium	2, 8, 1	Na^+
Fluorine	2, 7	F^-

[4 marks available — 1 mark for each correct answer.]

Pages 13-14: Ionic Compounds

1 a) strong (large also acceptable) *[1 mark]*, positive *[1 mark]*, negative *[1 mark]*, large *[1 mark]*, high *[1 mark]*.

b)

[1 mark for 8 electrons in sodium, 1 mark for 8 electrons in chlorine, 1 mark for both charges correct.]

c) positive — Al^{3+} *[1 mark]*, negative — F^- *[1 mark]*

2 a) Calcium chloride *[1 mark]* — ionic compounds have a high melting point *[1 mark]* due to the strong electrostatic attraction between the oppositely charged ions *[1 mark]*.

b) Magnesium oxide *[1 mark]* — the 2+ and 2− ions in magnesium oxide attract each other more strongly than the 1+ and 1− ions in sodium chloride *[1 mark]*. The stronger attraction means that more energy will be needed to break the bonds, leading to a higher boiling point *[1 mark]*.

c) i) It has a giant three-dimensional lattice structure *[1 mark]* which is held together by the attraction between the oppositely charged ions *[1 mark]*.

What's important for the first mark is that it's a giant structure.

   ii) diagram B *[1 mark]*

Pages 15-16: Covalent Bonding

1 a) 8 *[1 mark]*
   b) 3 *[1 mark]*
   c) 0 *[1 mark]*

All the bonds in the molecule are single covalent bonds — you get double bonds in molecules like ethene, oxygen and carbon dioxide.

2 a) i)   ii)   iii)

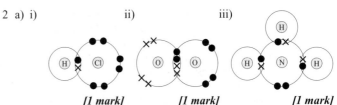

[1 mark]   *[1 mark]*   *[1 mark]*

b) A pair of electrons (one from the hydrogen atom and one from the chlorine atom) is shared between the two atoms *[1 mark]*. The atoms are held together by the strong attraction between this shared pair and the nuclei of the atoms *[1 mark]*.

3

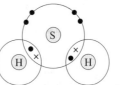

[2 marks available — 1 mark for the C-C shared pair, 1 mark for all of the H-C shared pairs correct]

4

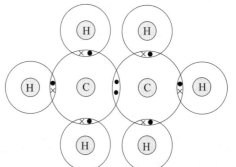

[2 marks available — 1 mark for both shared pairs, 1 mark for the non-bonding electrons.]

Pages 17-18: Covalent Substances

1 a) D *[1 mark]* — giant covalent substances have high melting points and don't normally conduct electricity, even when molten *[1 mark]*.

b) A *[1 mark]* — simple molecular substances have low melting points *[1 mark]*.

2 Low melting point — it is a simple molecular substance *[1 mark]* and so the intermolecular forces are weak and the molecules are easily parted from each other *[1 mark]*.

3 In a giant covalent structure, all of the atoms are bonded to each other with strong covalent bonds *[1 mark]*. It takes lots of energy to break the many bonds and melt the solid *[1 mark]*.

4 a) In graphite, each carbon atom only forms three covalent bonds, creating layers of carbon atoms *[1 mark]* which can slide over each other, making graphite useful as a lubricant *[1 mark]*.

b) In diamond, each carbon atom forms four covalent bonds in a very rigid structure *[1 mark]*. This makes diamond very hard, so it is good at cutting other substances *[1 mark]*.

c) i) B *[1 mark]*
   ii) D *[1 mark]*

Pages 19-20: Balancing Equations

1 a) Reactants: methane/CH_4 and oxygen/O_2 *[1 mark]*
      Products: carbon dioxide/CO_2 and water/H_2O *[1 mark]*

b) methane + oxygen → carbon dioxide + water *[1 mark]*

c) $CH_4 + 2O_2 \rightarrow CO_2 + 2H_2O$
   [1 mark for the correct reactants and products, 1 mark for correctly balancing the equation]

2 The third equation is correct ($2C + O_2 \rightarrow 2CO$) *[1 mark]*

3 a) i) $2HCl + CuO \rightarrow CuCl_2 + H_2O$ *[1 mark]*
 ii) $2HNO_3 + MgO \rightarrow Mg(NO_3)_2 + H_2O$ *[1 mark]*
 b) $6HCl + 2Al \rightarrow 2AlCl_3 + 3H_2$
 [1 mark for the correct reactants and products, 1 mark for correctly balancing the equation]
4 $Cl_2 + 2KBr \rightarrow Br_2 + 2KCl$
 [1 mark for the correct reactants and products, 1 mark for correctly balancing the equation]
5 a) $3CO + Fe_2O_3 \rightarrow 3CO_2 + 2Fe$ *[1 mark]*
 b) $2CuO + C \rightarrow 2Cu + CO_2$ *[1 mark]*
6 a) $2Na + Cl_2 \rightarrow 2NaCl$
 [1 mark for the correct reactants and products, 1 mark for correctly balancing the equation]
 b) $Ca(OH)_{2(aq)} + Na_2CO_{3(s)} \rightarrow 2NaOH_{(aq)} + CaCO_{3(s)}$
 [1 mark for all state symbols correct]
 c) $2Na_{(s)} + 2H_2O_{(l)} \rightarrow 2NaOH_{(aq)} + H_{2(g)}$
 [1 mark for correct reactants and products, 1 mark for correctly balancing the equation, 1 mark for all state symbols correct]

Page 21: Isotopes and Relative Atomic Mass

1 a) Isotopes are different atomic forms of the same element, which have the same number of protons *[1 mark]* but a different number of neutrons *[1 mark]*.
 b)

Isotope	Mass number	Number of protons	Number of neutrons
^{35}Cl	35	17	**18**
^{37}Cl	**37**	**17**	**20**

 [1 mark for correctly stating the mass number and number of protons in ^{37}Cl, 1 mark for correctly finding the number of neutrons in both ^{35}Cl and ^{37}Cl]
 As ^{35}Cl and ^{37}Cl are isotopes of the same element, they must have the same number of protons.
 c) i) The relative atomic mass is the average mass of all the isotopes of an element *[1 mark]* compared with the mass of one atom of carbon-12 *[1 mark]*.
 ii)
$$A_r = \frac{(35 \times 75) + (37 \times 25)}{75 + 25} = \textbf{35.5}$$
 [1 mark for (35×75)+(37×25), 1 mark for division by 100 (75+25), 1 mark for correct final answer]
 In the exam you might see the relative abundances of the isotopes given as percentages (as here), ratios or fractions. It doesn't matter what format the relative abundance numbers are in — you can just multiply them by the relative mass of each isotope and divide by the total of the relative abundances.

Page 22: Relative Formula Mass

1 $Ca(OH)_2 = 40 + (2 \times 16) + (2 \times 1)$ *[1 mark]* $= \textbf{74}$ *[1 mark]*
2 a) helium *[1 mark]*
 carbon *[1 mark]*
 3 × 4 = 12 and this is the A_r of carbon.
 oxygen *[1 mark]*
 4 × 4 = 16 and this is the A_r of oxygen.
 b) i) You know that the A_r of X = 12 and A_r of Y = 16 so:
 M_r of $XY_3 = 12 + (16 \times 3) = 60$ *[1 mark]*
 M_r of $Z_2 = 106 - 60 = 46$ *[1 mark]*
 A_r of Z = $46 \div 2 = \textbf{23}$ *[1 mark]*
 ii) Element Z is sodium/Na *[1 mark]*
 Element Z is sodium because 23 is the A_r of sodium.
3 $2AOH + H_2 = 114$
 $2A + (2 \times 16) + (2 \times 1) + (2 \times 1) = 114$
 $2A + 32 + 2 + 2 = 114$
 $2A + 36 = 114$
 $2A = 78$
 $A = 39$
 So element A = potassium *[1 mark for correct working, 1 mark for correct A_r, 1 mark for the correct final answer]*

Page 23: Empirical and Molecular Formulae

1 Division by A_r: N = $30.4 \div 14 = 2.17$
 O = $69.6 \div 16 = 4.35$ *[1 mark]*
 Simplest whole number ratio: 1:2 *[1 mark]*
 Empirical formula: NO_2 *[1 mark]*
2 Division by A_r: Al = $10.1 \div 27 = 0.37$
 Br = $89.9 \div 80 = 1.12$ *[1 mark]*
 Simplest whole number ratio: 1:3 *[1 mark]*
 Empirical formula: $AlBr_3$ *[1 mark]*
3 Work out the mass of H: $1.48 - (0.8 + 0.64) = 0.04$ *[1 mark]*
 Division by A_r: Ca = $0.8 \div 40 = 0.02$
 O = $0.64 \div 16 = 0.04$
 H = $0.04 \div 1 = 0.04$ *[1 mark]*
 Simplest whole number ratio: 1:2:2 *[1 mark]*
 Empirical formula: $Ca(OH)_2$ / CaO_2H_2 *[1 mark]*
4 Calculate the mass of the empirical formula:
 $(3 \times 12) + (7 \times 1) + (16) = 59$ *[1 mark]*
 Divide the relative molecular mass by this mass:
 $118 \div 59 = 2$ *[1 mark]*
 Work out the molecular formula:
 empirical formula $\times 2 = C_6H_{14}O_2$ *[1 mark]*

Pages 24-25: Calculating Masses in Reactions

1 a) 2Mg   2MgO
 $2 \times 24 = 48$ $2 \times (24 + 16) = 80$
 $48 \div 48 = 1$ g $80 \div 48 = 1.67$ g
 $1 \times 10 = 10$ g $1.67 \times 10 = \textbf{16.7 g}$
 [3 marks for correct final answer without any working, otherwise 1 mark for correctly calculating both M_rs and 1 mark for dividing through by 48 and multiplying by 10]
 b) 4Na $2Na_2O$
 $4 \times 23 = 92$ $2 \times [(2 \times 23) + 16] = 124$
 $92 \div 124 = 0.74$ g $124 \div 124 = 1$ g
 $0.74 \times 2 = \textbf{1.48 g}$ $1 \times 2 = 2$ g
 [3 marks for correct final answer without any working, otherwise 1 mark for correctly calculating both M_rs and 1 mark for dividing through by 124 and multiplying by 2]
2 a) Fe_2O_3 2Fe
 $(2 \times 56) + (3 \times 16) = 160$ $2 \times 56 = 112$
 $160 \div 160 = 1$ g $112 \div 160 = 0.7$ g
 $1 \times 20 = 20$ g $0.7 \times 20 = \textbf{14 g}$
 [3 marks for correct final answer without any working, otherwise 1 mark for correctly calculating both M_rs and 1 mark for dividing through by 160 and multiplying by 20]
 b) 2Al Fe_2O_3
 $2 \times 27 = 54$ $(2 \times 56) + (3 \times 16) = 160$
 $54 \div 160 = 0.3375$ kg $160 \div 160 = 1$ kg
 $0.3375 \times 32 = \textbf{10.8 kg}$ $1 \times 32 = 32$ kg
 [3 marks for correct final answer without any working, otherwise 1 mark for correctly calculating both M_rs and 1 mark for dividing through by 160 and multiplying by 32]
3 Mass of CO produced from 10 g of C at stage 2:
 C   2CO
 12                            $2 \times (12 + 16) = 56$
 $12 \div 12 = 1$ g $56 \div 12 = 4.67$ g
 $1 \times 10 = 10$ g $4.67 \times 10 = 46.7$ g
 Mass of CO_2 made from 46.7 g of CO at stage 3:
 3CO $3CO_2$
 $3 \times (12 + 16) = 84$ $3 \times [12 + (16 \times 2)] = 132$
 $84 \div 84 = 1$ g $132 \div 84 = 1.57$ g
 $1 \times 46.7 = 46.7$ g $1.57 \times 46.7 = \textbf{73.4 g}$
 [1 mark for working out the M_rs for stage 2, 1 mark for dividing them both by 12, 1 mark for finding correct mass of CO produced in stage 2. 1 mark for working out the M_rs for stage 3, 1 mark for dividing them both by 84, 1 mark for correct final answer.]

4 a)

2NaOH	Na$_2$SO$_4$
$2 \times (23 + 16 + 1) = 80$	$(2 \times 23) + 32 + (4 \times 16) = 142$
$80 \div 142 = 0.56$ g	$142 \div 142 = 1$ g
$0.56 \times 75 =$ **42.3 g**	$1 \times 75 = 75$ g

[3 marks for correct final answer without any working, otherwise 1 mark for correctly calculating both M$_r$s and 1 mark for dividing through by 142 and multiplying by 75]

b)

H$_2$SO$_4$	2H$_2$O
$(2 \times 1) + 32 + (4 \times 16) = 98$	$2 \times [(2 \times 1) + 16] = 36$
$98 \div 98 = 1$ g	$36 \div 98 = 0.367$ g
$1 \times 50 = 50$ g	$0.367 \times 50 =$ **18.4 g**

[3 marks for correct final answer without any working, otherwise 1 mark for correctly calculating both M$_r$s and 1 mark for dividing through by 98 and multiplying by 50]

Page 26: Percentage Yield

1 a) The yield of a reaction is the mass of product it produces *[1 mark]*.

b) i) percentage yield = (actual yield ÷ theoretical yield) × 100 *[1 mark]*

ii) percentage yield = (1.2 ÷ 2.7) × 100 = **44.4% *[1 mark]***

2 percentage yield = (6 ÷ 15) × 100 = **40% *[1 mark]***

3 A = (3.18 ÷ 3.33) × 100 = **95.5%**
B = (3.05 ÷ 3.33) × 100 = **91.6%**
C = (3.15 ÷ 3.33) × 100 = **94.6%**

[3 marks available — 1 mark for each correct percentage yield]

Page 27: Moles

1 a) 56 g *[1 mark]*

b) Avogadro's number / the Avogadro constant *[1 mark]*

2 a)
$$\text{number of moles} = \frac{\text{mass in grams}}{M_r} \quad \textit{[1 mark]}$$

b) i) $14 \div 7 =$ **2 moles** *[1 mark]*

ii) $112 \div 32 =$ **3.5 moles** *[1 mark]*

iii) $390 \div (28 + (16 \times 2)) =$ **6.5 moles** *[1 mark]*

iv) $275 \div (65 + 12 + (16 \times 3)) =$ **2.2 moles** *[1 mark]*

c) i) 59 g *[1 mark]*

ii) $2 \times 27 =$ **54 g** *[1 mark]*

iii) $6 \times (1 + 35.5) =$ **219 g** *[1 mark]*

iv) $4.5 \times (63.5 + 16) =$ **357.75 g** *[1 mark]*

3 Mass of 4 moles of KOH = $4 \times 56 = 224$ g *[1 mark]*
Extra mass needed = $224 - 140 =$ **84 g** *[1 mark]*

Page 28: Water of Crystallisation

1 a) E.g. to remove all of the water from the salt *[1 mark]*.

b) i) $61.224 - 53.500 =$ **7.724 g** *[1 mark]*

ii) $56.364 - 53.500 =$ **2.864 g** *[1 mark]*

c) M$_r$ of Na$_2$CO$_3$ = $(23 \times 2) + 12 + (16 \times 3) = 106$ *[1 mark]*
Moles of water lost:
Mass of water lost = $7.724 - 2.864 = 4.86$ g
Moles of water lost = $4.86 \div 18 = 0.27$ moles *[1 mark]*
Moles of anhydrous salt produced:
Moles of Na$_2$CO$_3$ = $2.864 \div 106 = 0.027$ moles *[1 mark]*
Ratio of salt to water:
0.027 moles of salt (Na$_2$CO$_3$) : 0.27 moles of water
1 mole of Na$_2$CO$_3$: (0.27 ÷ 0.027) = 10 moles of water
x = **10** *[1 mark]*

Page 29: Moles, Volume and Concentration

1 a) 24 dm^3 / 24 000 cm^3 *[1 mark]*

b) i) $1.5 \times 24 = 36$ dm^3 *[1 mark]*

ii) $2.25 \div 24 = 0.094$ moles OR $2250 \div 24\,000 = 0.094$ moles *[1 mark]*

c)

C	CO$_2$
12	44
$12 \div 12 = 1$	$44 \div 12 = 3.667$ *[1 mark]*
$1 \times 6.9 = 6.9$ g	$3.667 \times 6.9 = 25.3$ g

So 6.9 g of C gives 25.3 g of CO$_2$ *[1 mark]*
Volume = $(25.3 \div 44) \times 24$ *[1 mark]* = **13.8 dm^3** *[1 mark]*

2 a) $2.5 \times 0.125 = 0.3125$ moles *[1 mark]*

b) $3 \div 0.75 = 4$ mol/dm^3 *[1 mark]*

c) M$_r$ of Na$_2$SO$_4$ = $(23 \times 2) + 32 + (16 \times 4) = 142$ *[1 mark]*
Mass = $4 \times 142 = 568$ g
Concentration in g/dm^3 = **568 g/dm^3** *[1 mark]*

Page 30: Electrical Conductivity

1 a)

State	Conducts electricity? (yes/no)
Solid	No *[1 mark]*
Dissolved in water	Yes *[1 mark]*
Molten	Yes *[1 mark]*

b) When it is molten or in solution it conducts electricity because the ions separate and are free to move about *[1 mark]*, so they can carry electric current. When it is solid it doesn't conduct electricity because the ions are held rigidly and aren't free to move and carry electric current *[1 mark]*.

c) Electric current is a flow of electrons or ions *[1 mark]*.

d) E.g. covalent compounds make bonds by sharing electrons so they don't contain ions *[1 mark]*. This means that they don't have any charge carriers that are free to move and carry an electric current *[1 mark]*.

2 a) E.g. metals have a giant structure of positive ions surrounded by a sea of delocalised electrons *[1 mark]*.

b) E.g. metals are good conductors of electricity because the free electrons in the structure carry electrical current *[1 mark]*. Most metals are malleable because the layers of atoms in metals can slide over each other allowing them to be hammered or rolled into sheets *[1 mark]*.

Pages 31-32: Electrolysis

1 a) Pb^{2+}: **A**, molten lead: **C**, Br$^-$: **B**, Br$_2$: **D** *[2 marks for all letters correct, 1 mark for 2 or more letters correct]*

b) Negative electrode: Pb^{2+} + 2e$^-$ → Pb
[1 mark for correct equation, 1 mark for correct balancing]
Positive electrode: 2Br$^-$ → Br$_2$ + 2e$^-$
[1 mark for correct equation, 1 mark for correct balancing]

c) i) electrolytes *[1 mark]*

ii) E.g. you can place a conductivity probe into the substance *[1 mark]*. If a reading of zero conductivity is shown, the substance is a non-electrolyte *[1 mark]*. / You can set up an electrolytic cell *[1 mark]* and if the substance undergoes electrolysis then it is an electrolyte *[1 mark]*.

iii) It could be melted *[1 mark]*.

2 a) i) Negative electrode: Product = H$_2$/hydrogen, State = gas
[1 mark for product, 1 mark for state]
Positive electrode: Product = Cl$_2$/chlorine, State = gas
[1 mark for product, 1 mark for state]

ii) E.g. the metal ion, sodium (Na$^+$), is more reactive than the hydrogen ion (H$^+$) / hydrogen ions accept electrons more easily than sodium ions *[1 mark]*.

iii) Negative electrode: 2H$^+$ + 2e$^-$ → H$_2$
[1 mark for correct equation, 1 mark for correct balancing]
Positive electrode: 2Cl$^-$ → Cl$_2$ + 2e$^-$
[1 mark for correct equation, 1 mark for correct balancing]

b) Half-equation: 2H$^+$ + 2e$^-$ → H$_2$
Electrode: negative electrode
Half-equation: 4OH$^-$ → O$_2$ + 2H$_2$O + 4e$^-$
Electrode: positive electrode
[5 marks available — 1 mark for each correct equation, 1 mark for correctly balancing each equation, 1 mark for both electrodes correct]

c) i) Cu^{2+} *[1 mark]*, SO$_4^{2-}$ *[1 mark]*, H$^+$ *[1 mark]*, OH$^-$ *[1 mark]*

ii) Negative electrode: Cu/copper *[1 mark]*
Positive electrode: H$_2$O/water *[1 mark]*, O$_2$/oxygen *[1 mark]*

Page 33: Electrolysis — Calculating Masses

1

Metal ion	Number of moles of electrons	Number of faradays
Ca^{2+}	2	2
K^+	1	1
Al^{3+}	3	3

[1 mark for each correct answer]

2 a) $3.2 \times 20 = $ **64 C** *[1 mark]*

 b) $4320 \div 6 = 720$ seconds *[1 mark]*

 $720 \div 60 = $ **12 minutes** *[1 mark]*

Don't forget to look at the unit you need to give your answer in.
An answer of 720 seconds wouldn't get you full marks here.

3 a) $0.2 \times (40 \times 60) = 480$ C *[1 mark]*

 $480 \div 96\ 000 = $ **0.005 F** *[1 mark]*

 b)   0.005 mol *[1 mark]*

To get this answer you need to divide the number of faradays by the
number of electrons in the half-equation. Here you divide by 1, which is
why the answer is the same as the number of faradays.

 c) M_r of silver = 108. 108×0.005 *[1 mark]* = **0.54 g** *[1 mark]*

Section 2 — Chemistry of the Elements

Page 34: More About the Periodic Table

1 a)   a period *[1 mark]*

 b)   greater than 7 *[1 mark]*

 c) i)   The two elements will have similar properties *[1 mark]*

 ii)   To the right of the line *[1 mark]*. Since it does not conduct electricity, it must be a non-metal *[1 mark]*.

2 a)   Ca and Mg *[1 mark]*

If you put a cross in more than one box, you won't get the mark.

 b)   Na and K are in the same group so they have the same number of electrons in their outer shell *[1 mark]*.

 c)   They have a full outer shell of electrons *[1 mark]* so they don't need to lose or gain electrons in a reaction to obtain a full outer shell *[1 mark]*.

Page 35: Group 1 — The Alkali Metals

1 a)   Metal B is the most reactive *[1 mark]* because it takes the least time to react completely with the water *[1 mark]*.

 b)   A = sodium, B = potassium and C = lithium. *[2 marks for all three answers correct, otherwise 1 mark for any one answer correct.]*

 c)   sodium hydroxide *[1 mark]*, hydrogen *[1 mark]*

 d)   Rubidium is further down the group than potassium/metal B *[1 mark]*, so it is more reactive/will take less time to react *[1 mark]*.

2   As you go down Group 1, the outer electron is further from the nucleus *[1 mark]*, which means it is less strongly attracted to the nucleus *[1 mark]*. So as you go down Group 1 the outer electron is more easily lost *[1 mark]*.

Page 36: Group 7 — The Halogens

1 a)   Chlorine — green *[1 mark]*
 Iodine — solid *[1 mark]*

 b) i)   Fluorine is more reactive than chlorine *[1 mark]*.

 ii)   gas *[1 mark]*

2 a) $H_{2(g)} + Cl_{2(g)} \rightarrow 2HCl_{(g)}$
 [1 mark for the correct reactants and products, 1 mark for balancing the equation, 1 mark for correct state symbols.]

 b) i)   When hydrogen chloride is dissolved in water the molecules dissociate into H^+ ions and Cl^- ions *[1 mark]*. The H^+ ions make the solution acidic *[1 mark]*. When hydrogen chloride is dissolved in methylbenzene, it doesn't dissociate *[1 mark]*. There are no H^+ ions produced, so it's not acidic *[1 mark]*.

 ii)   hydrochloric acid *[1 mark]*

Page 37: Displacement Reactions

1 a)   A displacement reaction is where a more reactive element displaces a less reactive element from a compound *[1 mark]*.

 b) i) $Br_2 + 2KI \rightarrow I_2 + 2KBr$
 [1 mark for the correct reactants and products, 1 mark for balancing the equation.]

 ii)   E.g. Bromine is more reactive than iodine *[1 mark]*, so it will displace the iodine from the potassium iodide *[1 mark]*.

 c) i)   A reaction where reduction and oxidation happen at the same time, and so one substance loses electrons and another substance gains electrons *[1 mark]*.

 ii)   Bromine *[1 mark]*

Bromine goes from Br_2 to Br^- ions (in potassium bromide) during this
reaction. This means that the bromine is accepting electrons from the
iodide ions and being reduced — so it must be the oxidising agent.

2   Before — colourless *[1 mark]*
 After — orange *[1 mark]*

Pages 38-39: Reactions of Metals and the Reactivity Series

1 a) i)   aluminium sulfate *[1 mark]*, hydrogen *[1 mark]*

 ii)   Apply a lighted splint to a sample of the gas *[1 mark]*. If it burns with a squeaky pop, it must be hydrogen *[1 mark]*.

 b)   least vigorous $B \rightarrow A \rightarrow C \rightarrow D$ most vigorous
 [1 mark for two letters in the correct places in the order, 2 marks for all four letters in the correct places in the order.]

The clue is in the diagrams — the reaction that produces the most gas will
push the gas syringe out the furthest.

 c)   zinc *[1 mark]*

 d)   sodium + water $\rightarrow$ sodium hydroxide + hydrogen
 [1 mark for sodium hydroxide, 1 mark for hydrogen.]

It doesn't matter which way round you wrote the answers for this equation.

2 a)   iron / tin / lead *[1 mark]*

The unidentified metal must be more reactive than copper (as it displaces
copper from copper sulfate), but less reactive than zinc (which it doesn't
displace from zinc sulfate).

 b)   The copper was displaced from its salt *[1 mark]*.

3 a)

	aluminium oxide	copper oxide	iron oxide	magnesium oxide
aluminium	(✓)	✓	✓	✗
copper	✗	✗	✗	✗
iron	✗	✓	✗	✗
magnesium	✓	✓	(✗)	✗

[1 mark for circling aluminium/aluminium oxide, 1 mark for circling magnesium/iron oxide]

 b)   none *[1 mark]*

 c)   Metal: magnesium *[1 mark]*
 Reason: it is the most reactive metal in the table *[1 mark]*.

Page 40: Iron

1 a)   water *[1 mark]*, oxygen *[1 mark]*

Saying air instead of oxygen is unlikely to be specific enough to get the
marks for a question like this — always be as precise as you can.

 b)   tube B *[1 mark]*

 c)   The addition of oxygen / the loss of electrons *[1 mark]*.

 d)   The painted nail would not rust *[1 mark]*, because the paint creates a barrier that keeps out water and oxygen *[1 mark]*.

 e) i)   galvanising *[1 mark]*

 ii)   Zinc is more reactive than iron *[1 mark]*, so the zinc will be oxidised instead of the iron *[1 mark]*.

 f)   oiling *[1 mark]*

Page 41: Oxygen in the Atmosphere

1 a) i)   argon *[1 mark]*

 ii)   oxygen *[1 mark]*

 iii)   nitrogen *[1 mark]*

 b) i)   78% (accept 77-79%) *[1 mark]*

 ii)   0.04% (accept 0.035-0.045%) *[1 mark]*

2 Dry air is 21% oxygen
100% − 21% = 79%
50 cm^3 × 0.79 = **39.5 cm^3**
(accept 20-22% oxygen and a correctly calculated volume)
[2 marks for correct answer, otherwise 1 mark for using any correct method]

3 28.0 cm^3 − 21.7 cm^3 = 6.3 cm^3
(6.3 cm^3 ÷ 28.0 cm^3) × 100 = 22.5
22.5%
[2 marks for correct answer, otherwise 1 mark for using any correct method]

Page 42: Oxygen in Reactions

1 a) $2H_2O_{2(aq)} \rightarrow 2H_2O_{(l)} + O_{2(g)}$
[1 mark for correct formulas of reactant and products including their state symbols, 1 mark for correctly balancing the equation.]
You'd still get the marks for any multiple of the balanced equation in a question like this (for example $H_2O_{2(aq)} \rightarrow H_2O_{(l)} + \frac{1}{2}O_{2(g)}$).

 b) i) 17 cm^3 *[1 mark]*
  ii) Any one from: e.g. use a delivery tube to bubble gas into an upside-down measuring cylinder filled with water. / Use a gas syringe. *[1 mark]*
  iii) Manganese(IV) oxide was the most effective catalyst *[1 mark]* because it led to the greatest volume of oxygen being produced over the time period measured/increased the rate of reaction by the greatest amount *[1 mark]*.

2

Element	Flame colour when burnt	Oxide formed	Acid-base character of oxide
sodium	Yellow-orange	Na_2O	Alkaline
magnesium	White	MgO	Slightly alkaline
carbon	Orange/yellow	CO_2	Slightly acidic
sulfur	Blue	SO_2	Acidic

[1 mark for each correct answer]

Page 43: Preparation of Carbon Dioxide

1 a) E.g. the delivery tube needs to feed downwards into an upright test tube *[1 mark]*. Carbon dioxide is more dense than air, so it will displace the air and collect in the tube/it cannot be collected in an upside-down test tube *[1 mark]*.
You can have the first mark here for any other sensible suggestion, like swapping the test tube for a gas syringe.
 b) copper oxide *[1 mark]*
 c) thermal decomposition *[1 mark]*
2 a) $CaCO_3 + 2HCl \rightarrow CaCl_2 + H_2O + CO_2$ *[1 mark]*
 b) E.g. use dilute acid / wear safety goggles / wear gloves / wear a lab coat *[1 mark]*.
Anything you might do to protect yourself from acid burns will do here.

Page 44: Carbon Dioxide — the Good and the Bad

1 a) i) slightly *[1 mark]*, released *[1 mark]*
  ii) denser *[1 mark]*, oxygen *[1 mark]*
 b) Heat detector B *[1 mark]*, e.g. because the nitrogen will absorb less heat than the carbon dioxide/the carbon dioxide will absorb more heat than the nitrogen *[1 mark]*.
 c) Carbon dioxide absorbs heat that would otherwise be radiated out into space *[1 mark]* and re-radiates some of it back towards the Earth *[1 mark]*.
 d) i) The temperature increased *[1 mark]*.
  ii) E.g. climate change / changing rainfall patterns / sea level rise / flooding *[1 mark]*
Be careful — you can't say 'global warming' here because that's just an alternative name for the temperature change, not an effect of it.

Pages 45-46: Tests for Cations

1 a) E.g. take a clean platinum wire loop, dip it into the substance to be tested and put the material into the hot part of a Bunsen burner flame.
[1 mark for any suitable method stated to transfer the material into the flame, 1 mark for saying that the material needs to be placed in the flame]
 b) Potassium would give a lilac flame *[1 mark]* but sodium would give a yellow-orange flame *[1 mark]*.
 c) The medicines also contain sodium ions *[1 mark]*, so the colour produced by the sodium could interfere with the flame test result *[1 mark]*.

2 a)

Metal ion	Colour of precipitate
Fe^{2+}	green
Cu^{2+}	blue
Fe^{3+}	reddish brown

[1 mark for each ion or colour]
 b) $Fe^{2+}_{(aq)} + 2OH^-_{(aq)} \rightarrow Fe(OH)_{2(s)}$ *[1 mark]*
 c) $Fe^{3+}_{(aq)} + 3OH^-_{(aq)} \rightarrow Fe(OH)_{3(s)}$
[1 mark for the reactants and product, 1 mark for the state symbols, 1 mark for balancing the equation.]
3 a) i) LiCl *[1 mark]*
  ii) $CaCl_2$ *[1 mark]*
  iii) $CuSO_4$ *[1 mark]*
  iv) $(NH_4)_2SO_4$ *[1 mark]*
 b) Use a piece of red litmus paper *[1 mark]* which has been dampened *[1 mark]*. If there's ammonia present, the litmus paper will turn blue *[1 mark]*.
 c) E.g. wear goggles / make sure the laboratory is well-ventilated / do the test in a fume cupboard *[1 mark]*
This time it's anything you might do to protect yourself from chemical burns, or from breathing in the ammonia vapour.

Page 47: Tests for Anions

1 a) i) SO_4^{2-} *[1 mark]*
  ii) I^- *[1 mark]*
  iii) CO_3^{2-} *[1 mark]*
 b) i) dilute hydrochloric acid *[1 mark]*, barium chloride solution *[1 mark]*
  ii) a white precipitate *[1 mark]*
 c) i) e.g. dilute hydrochloric acid *[1 mark]*
Any dilute acid will do here — you'd usually use hydrochloric, but sulfuric or nitric would work too.
  ii) carbon dioxide *[1 mark]*
 d) Add dilute nitric acid *[1 mark]* followed by silver nitrate solution *[1 mark]*. Chloride ions will give a white precipitate *[1 mark]* whereas bromide ions will give a cream precipitate *[1 mark]*.
 e) i) Cl^- *[1 mark]*
  ii) SO_4^{2-} *[1 mark]*

Page 48: Tests for Gases and Water

1 a) Test the gas with a lighted splint *[1 mark]*. Hydrogen will burn with a squeaky pop *[1 mark]*.
 b) Test the gas with a glowing splint *[1 mark]*. Oxygen will relight it *[1 mark]*.
2 a) i) white *[1 mark]*
  ii) The white powder would turn blue *[1 mark]*.
 b) Pure water has a boiling point of 100 °C *[1 mark]* and a freezing point of 0 °C *[1 mark]*, so the liquid cannot be pure water *[1 mark]*.
 c) Chlorine gas bleaches damp litmus paper *[1 mark]*. Carbon dioxide gas turns limewater cloudy *[1 mark]*. So the gas does contain carbon dioxide *[1 mark]* but it doesn't contain chlorine *[1 mark]*.

Section 3 — Organic Chemistry

Page 49: Alkanes

1 a) A hydrocarbon is a molecule/compound that is made up of hydrogen and carbon atoms *[1 mark]* only *[1 mark]*.

b) i) C_nH_{2n+2} *[1 mark]*

A general formula means you can replace the 'n's with a number to get the formula of a certain molecule in the series — so the 4th alkane is $C_4H_{(2\times4+2)} = C_4H_{10}$.

ii) homologous series *[1 mark]*

c)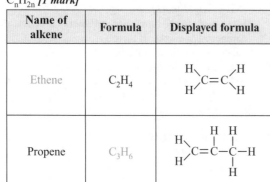

[1 mark]

d) methane + bromine $\xrightarrow{\text{UV}}$ bromomethane + hydrogen bromide *[1 mark for each correct product]*

It doesn't matter which way round you write the two missing answers here, but you must get them both right to get the mark.

2 a) E.g. in a saturated molecule all of the atoms are bonded to as many other atoms as they can be / all of the bonds are single covalent bonds *[1 mark]*.

b) i) $2C_4H_{10} + 13O_2 \rightarrow 8CO_2 + 10H_2O$
[1 mark for formulas of all reactants and products correct, 1 mark for equation being correctly balanced]

ii) carbon monoxide *[1 mark]*, carbon *[1 mark]*

Page 50: Alkenes

1 a) C_nH_{2n} *[1 mark]*

b)

Name of alkene	Formula	Displayed formula
Ethene	C_2H_4	H₂C=CH₂ (displayed)
Propene	C_3H_6	CH₂=CH–CH₃ (displayed)

[4 marks available — 1 mark for each correct name or formula]

The displayed formula for propene could also be drawn with the double bond between the second and third carbon atoms. As long as you've got the right number of hydrogen atoms attached to each carbon atom, it doesn't matter which two carbons the double bond is between.

2 a) i) butene *[1 mark]*

ii) C and D *[1 mark]*

Isomers have identical molecular formulas but different structures — these are both C_4H_8.

b) i) before — orange, after — colourless *[1 mark]*

ii) The C=C double bond in pentene is split *[1 mark]* and a bromine atom is added to each of these two carbon atoms *[1 mark]*.

Pages 51-52: Ethanol

1 a) $C_2H_5OH \rightarrow C_2H_4 + H_2O$ *[1 mark]*

b) a dehydration reaction *[1 mark]*

c) aluminium oxide *[1 mark]*

2 a)

Method	Reaction	Temperature needed
A	$C_2H_4 + \mathbf{H_2O} \rightarrow C_2H_5OH$	300 °C
B	$C_6H_{12}O_6 \rightarrow 2CO_2 + \mathbf{2}C_2H_5OH$	about 30 °C

[4 marks available — 1 mark for each reaction or temperature]

b) fermentation *[1 mark]*

c) Pressure — 60-70 atmospheres *[1 mark]*
Catalyst — phosphoric acid *[1 mark]*

d) Method A *[1 mark]* — crude oil is the raw material from which ethene is made, and there is a good supply for country Z. / If country Z has a very cold climate, sugar cane probably won't grow well, and this is the raw material for method B *[1 mark]*.

3 a) i) ethene *[1 mark]*

ii) crude oil *[1 mark]*

b) i) E.g. it uses a low temperature/simple equipment, which is cheap. / The raw materials are renewable *[1 mark]*.

ii) E.g. the ethanol needs to be concentrated/purified. / Labour costs are high *[1 mark]*.

c) i)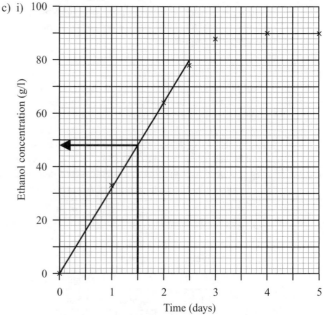

[2 marks for plotting all 4 points correctly, 1 mark for plotting at least 3 points correctly, 1 mark for the line of best fit.]

ii) 48 g/l (allow 47-49 g/l) *[1 mark]*

Section 4 — Physical Chemistry

Page 53: Acids and Alkalis

1 a) 0 to 14 *[1 mark]*

b) neutral *[1 mark]*

c) strong alkali *[1 mark]*

2

Indicator	Colour
Litmus paper	blue
Phenolphthalein	pink
Universal indicator	purple
Methyl orange	yellow

[3 marks for whole table correct, otherwise 1 mark for each correct answer]

3 a) H^+ ions/hydrogen ions *[1 mark]*

b) neutralisation *[1 mark]*

c) The solution will turn green (because universal indicator is green in neutral solutions) *[1 mark]*.

Page 54: Reactions of Acids

1 a) magnesium sulfate + water *[1 mark]*
  b) aluminium chloride + hydrogen *[1 mark]*
2 a) nitric acid + copper oxide → copper nitrate + water
    [1 mark]
  b) $2HCl + Zn → ZnCl_2 + H_2$ *[1 mark for the correct formulae, 1 mark for correct balancing]*
  c) sulfuric acid *[1 mark]*
3 a) carbon dioxide *[1 mark]*
Don't just give the formula of carbon dioxide — the question asks you to name the gas.
  b) $2HNO_3 + CaCO_3 → Ca(NO_3)_2 + H_2O + CO_2$ *[1 mark for the correct formulae, 1 mark for correct balancing]*
  c) hydrochloric acid *[1 mark]*

Pages 55-56: Making Salts

1 a) soluble *[1 mark]*
  b) acids *[1 mark]*
  c) insoluble *[1 mark]*, sodium *[1 mark]*
2 a) B *[1 mark]*
  b) C *[1 mark]*
  c) A *[1 mark]*
3 a) calcium nitrate *[1 mark]*, potassium sulfate *[1 mark]*
You can't use barium sulfate or calcium carbonate because they are both insoluble, so cannot be dissolved to make solutions.
  b) Filter the mixture (to separate the solid calcium sulfate from the liquid) *[1 mark]*.
4 a) Any one from: the excess of silver carbonate will sink to the bottom of the flask and stay there / the mixture will stop producing bubbles (of carbon dioxide) *[1 mark]*.
  b) silver carbonate + nitric acid → silver nitrate + water + carbon dioxide *[1 mark]*
  c) filtration *[1 mark]*
  d) Evaporate off the water *[1 mark]*.
  e) i) Potassium hydroxide is soluble, so you can't tell/see when the reaction is finished *[1 mark]*. This means you can't add an excess of solid to the acid and filter out what's left *[1 mark]*.
    ii) E.g. work out exactly how much potassium hydroxide is needed to neutralise the nitric acid by gradually measuring out the alkali into a known volume of the acid
      [1 mark] and using an indicator to show when the reaction has finished/neutralisation has occurred *[1 mark]*.
      Repeat the reaction using exactly the same volumes of acid and alkali, but no indicator, to produce the pure solution
      [1 mark].

Page 57: Titrations

1 a) $Ca(OH)_2 + 2HCl → CaCl_2 + 2H_2O$ *[1 mark for the correct products, 1 mark for correct balancing]*
  b) $0.1 × (20 ÷ 1000)$ *[1 mark]*
    = **0.002 moles** *[1 mark]*
    [Allow 2 marks for correct answer without working]
  c) $0.002 ÷ 2 =$ **0.001 moles** *[1 mark]*
  d) $0.001 ÷ (50 ÷ 1000)$ *[1 mark]*
    = **0.02 mol/dm³** *[1 mark]*
    [Allow 2 marks for correct answer without working]
  e) M_r of $Ca(OH)_2$ is $(1 × 40) + (2 × 16) + (2 × 1) = 74$ *[1 mark]*
    Concentration = $0.02 × 74 =$ **1.48 g/dm³** *[1 mark]*
    [Allow 2 marks for correct answer without working]
2 a) Moles KOH = $0.1 × (30 ÷ 1000)$ *[1 mark]*
    = **0.003** *[1 mark]*
    Reaction equation shows that 2 moles of KOH react with 1 mole of H_2SO_4 so 0.003 moles of KOH react with
    $0.003 ÷ 2 = 0.0015$ moles of H_2SO_4 *[1 mark]*
    Concentration = $0.0015 ÷ (10 ÷ 1000)$ *[1 mark]*
    = **0.15 mol/dm³** *[1 mark]*
There are 0.0015 moles in 10 cm³ of H_2SO_4. So you need to calculate how many moles there are in 1 dm³ (1000 cm³) to get the concentration.
  b) M_r of H_2SO_4 is $(2 × 1) + (1 × 32) + (4 × 16) = 98$ *[1 mark]*
    Concentration = $0.15 × 98 =$ **14.7 g/dm³** *[1 mark]*
    [Allow 2 marks for correct answer without working]

Page 58: Rates of Reaction

1 a) Z *[1 mark]*. It has the steepest initial gradient. / It flattens off earliest *[1 mark]*.
  b) Equal quantities of marble chips were used in each experiment (and the acid was in excess) *[1 mark]*.
  c) It decreases *[1 mark]*
  d) i) Curve C, as below. The curve should initially be steeper than the original curve (grey), and should end at the same change in mass *[1 mark]*.
    ii) Curve L, as below. The curve should initially be less steep than the original curve (grey), and should end at the same change in mass *[1 mark]*.

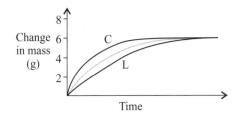

Pages 59-60: Measuring Rates of Reaction

1 a) i) E.g. it is very accurate (because the mass balance is accurate) *[1 mark]*.
    ii) E.g. the gas is released directly into the room and may be toxic/hazardous *[1 mark]*.
  b) i) E.g. observe a marker through the solution *[1 mark]*. Measure how long it takes for the marker to disappear (as the precipitate forms) *[1 mark]*.
    ii) E.g. it only works for reactions where the initial solution is transparent / the result is subjective as it depends on deciding when the marker has disappeared
      [1 mark].
2 a) $2H_2O_2 → 2H_2O + O_2$
    [1 mark for the correct reactants and products, 1 mark for correct balancing]
  b) Measuring the volume of gas produced at regular intervals *[1 mark]*.
3 a) 50 in the third column of the table should be circled *[1 mark]*.
  b)

Average volume of gas produced (cm³)
94
64
45.5
20
9

[1 mark for at least 3 values correct, 2 marks for all 5 values correct]

Don't forget that you need to ignore anomalous results when calculating averages. So you shouldn't include the result of 50 cm³ at the concentration of 0.5 mol/dm³.

  c) i) 2 mol/dm³ *[1 mark]*
    ii) It produced the largest volume of gas in the given time *[1 mark]*.
  d) i) Gas syringe *[1 mark]*
    ii) Any one from: stopwatch (accept e.g. stopclock/timer) / balance / measuring cylinder (or equivalent, e.g. burette) *[1 mark]*
  e) To improve the reliability of his results *[1 mark]*.
  f) Any one from: e.g. misreading the value from the gas syringe / not emptying the gas syringe before starting / measuring out incorrect quantities of reactants / measuring the time period of the experiment incorrectly *[1 mark]*.

Pages 61-64: Rate of Reaction Experiments

1 a)   A *[1 mark]*
  b)   Curve C, as below. The curve should be between curves A and B *[1 mark]*.

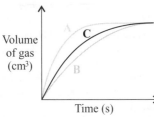

  c) i) E.g. the teacher would have used the same volume / concentration of acid in each experiment *[1 mark]*. This variable is controlled so that you can tell if the variable you're changing is causing the results *[1 mark]*.
     ii) E.g. yes *[1 mark]*, because the same volume of gas was produced in each experiment *[1 mark]*.

This suggests that either the same volume of acid, or an excess of acid, was used in both experiments.

  d)   Measuring how quickly the reaction loses mass *[1 mark]*.

2 a)

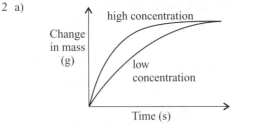

[1 mark for each correct line]
The high concentration curve should go up more steeply and flatten out earlier than the low concentration curve, but both curves should end at the same point.

  b) i) E.g. acid spitting/splashing during the reaction *[1 mark]*.
     ii) E.g. wearing safety goggles/gloves to protect the eyes/hands *[1 mark]*.

3 a)   1 *[1 mark]*, because the initial slope of the graph is steepest *[1 mark]*.
  b)   All of the reactions finish eventually because at least one of the reactants is always used up *[1 mark]*.

4 a)   The solution turns cloudy *[1 mark]*.
  b) i) The rate of reaction increases *[1 mark]*.
     ii) 145 s *[1 mark]*
  c)   Repeat the investigation to get more results and find the average for each temperature *[1 mark]*.
  d)   Increasing the concentration of hydrochloric acid/HCl increases the rate of reaction / decreasing the concentration of hydrochloric acid/HCl decreases the rate of reaction *[1 mark]*.

5   The rate of reaction depends on the acid concentration *[1 mark]*.

6 a)   R *[1 mark]*. It has the steepest graph and flattens off soonest, so it is the fastest reaction *[1 mark]*.
  b)   E.g. temperature / the volume/mass of H_2O_2 / the concentration of H_2O_2 *[1 mark]*.

Page 65: Collision Theory

1 a)   Increasing the pressure means there are more particles/molecules/atoms of gas in a given volume/space / the particles are closer together *[1 mark]* so collisions happen more frequently *[1 mark]*.
  b) i) activation energy *[1 mark]*
     ii) By increasing the temperature *[1 mark]*.
2 a) i) The one that uses powdered magnesium carbonate *[1 mark]*.
     ii) The powdered magnesium carbonate has a larger surface area *[1 mark]*. This means the particles will collide with it more often/more frequently *[1 mark]*.

  b)   A lower concentration would have fewer reactant particles in a certain volume. / The particles would be further apart in a lower concentration *[1 mark]*. This means that particles would collide less frequently *[1 mark]*.

Pages 66-67: Energy Transfer in Reactions

1   endothermic, exothermic, greater, given out to, taken in from *[1 mark for each correct answer]*
2 a)   Endothermic *[1 mark]*. The temperature decrease shows that the reaction is taking in energy from the surroundings *[1 mark]*.
  b)   A–B *[1 mark]*, because the reaction is endothermic and so more heat energy is taken in when this bond is broken than is released when the A–C bond is formed *[1 mark]*.
  c) i) The overall change in energy during a reaction *[1 mark]*.
     ii) positive *[1 mark]*
     iii) ΔH *[1 mark]*
3 a)   Energy is given out *[1 mark]*.
  b)   Exothermic *[1 mark]* because it gives out heat to the surroundings *[1 mark]*.
  c) i) −890.3 kJ/mol *[1 mark]*
     ii) The enthalpy change of an exothermic reaction is negative because the reaction is giving out energy *[1 mark]*.
4 a)   Endothermic *[1 mark]* because it requires heating/takes in energy from the surroundings / because the reverse reaction is favoured by a lower temperature *[1 mark]*.
  b)   negative *[1 mark]*

Page 68: Energy Level Diagrams

1 a)   endothermic *[1 mark]*
  b)   The minimum energy needed by reacting particles for a reaction to occur *[1 mark]*.
  c)   They provide a different pathway with a lower activation energy *[1 mark]*.
2 a) i) A / C / D *[1 mark]*
     ii) B / E *[1 mark]*
     iii) C *[1 mark]*
     iv) B *[1 mark]*
  b) i) −90 kJ/mol *[1 mark]*
     ii) 70 kJ/mol *[1 mark]*
     iii) The curve should start and end at the same energy level as the original curve (grey), but have a lower peak/activation energy *[1 mark]*.

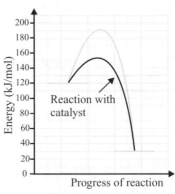

Page 69: Bond Energy Calculations

1      $(4 \times 412) + (2 \times 498) = 2644$ kJ/mol *[1 mark]*
       $(2 \times 743) + (4 \times 463) = 3338$ kJ/mol *[1 mark]*
       Enthalpy change = 2644 − 3338 = **−694 kJ/mol** *[1 mark for correct value, 1 mark for correct sign]*
2      $158 + (4 \times 391) + 498 = 2220$ kJ/mol *[1 mark]*
       $945 + (4 \times 463) = 2797$ kJ/mol *[1 mark]*
       Enthalpy change = 2220 − 2797 = **−577 kJ/mol** *[1 mark for correct value, 1 mark for correct sign]*

Pages 70-71: Enthalpy Changes

1 a) To ensure that they are the same temperature before beginning the reaction / to know their initial temperature *[1 mark]*.
   b) i) To insulate the cup *[1 mark]*.
      ii) To reduce the energy lost by evaporation *[1 mark]*.
   c) 31 °C – 21 °C = **10 °C** *[1 mark]*
   d) i) Some energy is always lost to the surroundings *[1 mark]*.
      ii) The experiment could be repeated and an average temperature change calculated *[1 mark]*.
   e) E.g. dissolving (or dissolution) / displacement *[1 mark]*.
2 a) Because copper conducts heat very well *[1 mark]*.
   b) heat energy change = $50 \times 4.2 \times 30.5$ = **6405 J** *[1 mark]*
   c) Energy produced = $6405 \div 0.7$ *[1 mark]*
      = 9150 J/g = **9.15 kJ/g** *[1 mark]*
3 a) M_r of ethanol = $(2 \times 12) + (6 \times 1) + (1 \times 16)$ = 46 *[1 mark]*
      Number of moles = $1.15 \div 46$ = **0.025** *[1 mark]*
   b) Molar enthalpy change = $-7.245 \div 0.025$ *[1 mark]*
      = **–289.8 kJ/mol** *[1 mark]*
The enthalpy change (–7.245 kJ) is negative because combustion is an exothermic reaction.

Pages 72-73: Reversible Reactions

1 a) It is reversible *[1 mark]*.
   b) Both (the forward and reverse) reactions are taking place *[1 mark]* at exactly the same rate *[1 mark]*.
   c) i) It takes in heat *[1 mark]*, because it's endothermic/all reversible reactions are exothermic in one direction and endothermic in the other direction. *[1 mark]*
      ii) One reaction is always exothermic and the other endothermic *[1 mark]*, so a change in temperature will always favour one reaction more than the other *[1 mark]*.
      iii) left *[1 mark]*
   d) It won't affect the position of equilibrium *[1 mark]*, because there are the same number of molecules on either side of the equation *[1 mark]*.
Make sure you talk about the number of moles/molecules in your answer — if you only mention volume you won't get the mark.
   e) It is not a closed system / the products can escape *[1 mark]*.
2 a) Endothermic *[1 mark]*, because it is favoured by heating/heat is taken in *[1 mark]*.
   b) i) It turns from white to blue *[1 mark]*.
      ii) It increases *[1 mark]*.
3 The first student's reaction conditions are better *[1 mark]*, because:
   The forward reaction is endothermic *[1 mark]* so raising the temperature will increase this reaction to use up the extra heat *[1 mark]*. There are more molecules/moles on the right-hand side of the equation *[1 mark]*, and a lower pressure will encourage the reaction that produces more molecules/moles *[1 mark]*.

Section 5 — Chemistry in Industry

Page 74: Metal Ores

1 a) Iron is lower in the reactivity series than carbon *[1 mark]*, so carbon can take oxygen away from iron *[1 mark]*.
   b) reduction *[1 mark]*
   c) iron(III) oxide + carbon → iron + carbon dioxide *[1 mark]*
2 a) $2ZnO + C \rightarrow 2Zn + CO_2$ *[1 mark for correct reactants and products, 1 mark for correct balancing]*
   b) The reducing agent is carbon *[1 mark]*.
3 a) electrolysis *[1 mark]*
   b) If the metal is more reactive than carbon, it can't be extracted using carbon *[1 mark]*.

Page 75: Extracting Aluminium

1 a) i) The cost of electricity / a lot of electricity is needed *[1 mark]*.
      ii) It reduces the temperature needed to carry out the electrolysis *[1 mark]*, which makes the process cheaper to run *[1 mark]*.
   b) $Al^{3+} + 3e^- \rightarrow Al$
      $2O^{2-} \rightarrow O_2 + 4e^-$
      [3 marks available — 1 mark for correct aluminium equation, 1 mark for correct oxygen equation, 1 mark for correct balancing of both equations]
   c) They are reduced *[1 mark]*, because they gain electrons *[1 mark]*.
   d) The positive electrode *[1 mark]*, because it is getting constantly worn down by reacting with the oxygen that is produced at that electrode *[1 mark]*.

Pages 76-77: Extracting Iron

1 a) i) haematite *[1 mark]*
      ii) coke *[1 mark]*, limestone *[1 mark]*
   b) Label A: molten iron *[1 mark]*.
      Label B: molten slag *[1 mark]*.
   c) Air is blown into the furnace to make the coke burn faster than usual and raise the temperature to about 1500 °C *[1 mark]*.
2 a) i) $C + O_2 \rightarrow CO_2$ *[1 mark]*
      $CO_2 + C \rightarrow 2CO$ *[1 mark]*
      ii) The coke burns and produces carbon dioxide/CO_2 *[1 mark]*. The carbon dioxide/CO_2 then reacts with unburnt coke to produce carbon monoxide/CO *[1 mark]*.
   b) i) $3CO + Fe_2O_3 \rightarrow 3CO_2 + 2Fe$
      [2 marks available — 1 mark for the correct reactants and products, 1 mark for correctly balancing the equation]
      ii) reduced *[1 mark]*
3 a) sand/silicon dioxide/SiO_2 *[1 mark]*
   b) $CaCO_3 \rightarrow CaO + CO_2$ *[1 mark]*
   c) $CaO + SiO_2 \rightarrow CaSiO_3$ *[1 mark]*

Page 78: Uses of Iron and Aluminium

1 a) Any three from: e.g. they are both lustrous / both have high tensile strength/are strong / are both malleable / are both good conductors of electricity / are both good conductors of heat *[Maximum of 3 marks available — 1 mark for each property]*.
   b) E.g. aluminium is much less dense than iron, which means aeroplanes can be made lighter and therefore more efficient / unlike iron, aluminium doesn't corrode, which is important as the aeroplane will come into contact with water if it rains *[1 mark]*.
2 a) Steel *[1 mark]*. It has very good malleability so it can be shaped easily *[1 mark]*.
   b) E.g. it is resistant to corrosion/doesn't rust *[1 mark]*.

Page 79: Fractional Distillation of Crude Oil

1 a) hydrocarbons *[1 mark]*
   b) gas *[1 mark]*, lower *[1 mark]*, condense *[1 mark]*, up *[1 mark]*.
   c)

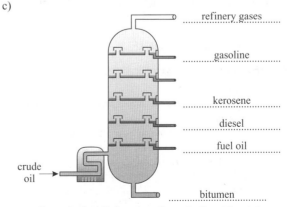

[3 marks for all 6 correct, 2 marks for at least 4 correct, 1 mark for at least 2 correct]

d)   bitumen *[1 mark]*

e)   E.g. the longer the molecule, the higher the boiling point of the fraction *[1 mark]*.

f)   Any one from: e.g. for domestic central heating / as fuel for ships *[1 mark]*

Page 80: Pollutants

1 a)   Carbon monoxide can form if the fuel is burnt without enough oxygen / if incomplete combustion occurs *[1 mark]*.

b)   Carbon monoxide can interfere with the blood's role of carrying oxygen around the body, meaning it can carry less *[1 mark]*.

2 a) i)   high temperatures *[1 mark]*

  ii)   E.g. in a car engine *[1 mark]*.

b)   nitric acid *[1 mark]*

c) i)   sulfur dioxide *[1 mark]*

  ii)   E.g. lakes become acidic and plants and animals can die as a result / trees are killed *[1 mark for each correct answer]*.

Page 81: Cracking Hydrocarbons

1 a)   There is a greater demand for short-chain hydrocarbons than for longer-chain hydrocarbons *[1 mark]*. To meet this demand, long hydrocarbons are split into more useful short-chain molecules *[1 mark]*. Cracking also produces alkenes *[1 mark]* which are used to make polymers/plastic *[1 mark]*.

b) i)   The paraffin is soaked into the mineral wool *[1 mark]*.

  ii)   It acts as a catalyst / catalyses the reaction *[1 mark]*.

  iii)   alkenes *[1 mark]*

2 a) $C_{10}H_{22} \rightarrow C_8H_{18} + C_2H_4$ *[1 mark]*

b)   600–700 °C *[1 mark]*

Page 82: Addition Polymers

1   monomers *[1 mark]*

2 a)   ethene *[1 mark]*

b) i)

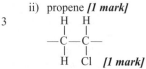

[1 mark]

Don't worry if you put the CH_3 in another position — as long as it's attached to one of the carbon atoms, it's still correct.

  ii)   propene *[1 mark]*

3

$$-\overset{\overset{\displaystyle H}{|}}{\underset{\underset{\displaystyle H}{|}}{C}}-\overset{\overset{\displaystyle H}{|}}{\underset{\underset{\displaystyle Cl}{|}}{C}}-$$
[1 mark]

The chlorine atom can be attached to any one of the carbon atoms.

Page 83: More on Polymers and Their Uses

1 a)   E.g. packaging / plastic bags / plastic bottles / plastic containers *[1 mark]*.

b)   E.g. kettles / food containers *[1 mark]*.

c)   E.g. clothes / insulation for electrical cables *[1 mark]*

2   E.g. most addition polymers are inert/don't react easily *[1 mark]*. This means that it takes a very long time for them to biodegrade and they can stay unchanged in landfill sites for a long time *[1 mark]*.

3 a)   condensation polymerisation *[1 mark]*

b)   water *[1 mark]*, H_2O *[1 mark]*

Page 84: The Haber Process

1 a) $N_2 + 3H_2 \rightleftharpoons 2NH_3$
[1 mark for correct reactants and products, 1 mark for correct balancing]

b)   Reactant 1: nitrogen *[1 mark]* Source: the air *[1 mark]*
Reactant 2: hydrogen *[1 mark]* Source: natural gas/cracking of hydrocarbons *[1 mark]*

It doesn't matter which way round you have your reactants.
Each one just needs to be matched up with a correct source.

c)   E.g. nitric acid *[1 mark]* and fertiliser *[1 mark]*

2 a)   Temperature used: 450 °C *[1 mark]*
Pressure used: 200 atm *[1 mark]*

b)   iron *[1 mark]*

c)   E.g. as the ammonia gas cools it condenses and liquefies *[1 mark]*, which means it is separated from the other gases and can be easily piped off *[1 mark]*. The unused hydrogen and nitrogen are recycled/re-circulated/pumped back into the reaction chamber to be used in the reaction again *[1 mark]*.

Page 85: The Contact Process

1

Temperature	450 °C *[1 mark]*
Pressure	2 atmospheres/atm *[1 mark]*
Catalyst	vanadium(V) oxide/V_2O_5 *[1 mark]*

2 a)   Equation: $S + O_2 \rightarrow SO_2$ *[1 mark]*
Description: sulfur is burned in air to form sulfur dioxide gas *[1 mark]*.

b)   Equation: $2SO_2 + O_2 \rightleftharpoons 2SO_3$ *[1 mark for correct reactants and products, 1 mark for correct balancing]*
Description: the sulfur dioxide is reacted with oxygen/ oxidised to form sulfur trioxide *[1 mark]*.

c)   Equation: $SO_3 + H_2SO_4 \rightarrow H_2S_2O_7$ *[1 mark]*
Description: sulfur trioxide is dissolved in sulfuric acid to form oleum *[1 mark]*.

d)   Equation: $H_2S_2O_7 + H_2O \rightarrow 2H_2SO_4$
[1 mark for correct reactants and products, 1 mark for correct balancing]
Description: oleum is diluted with water to form concentrated sulfuric acid *[1 mark]*.

3   E.g. it's used to make fertilisers *[1 mark]*, detergents *[1 mark]* and paints *[1 mark]*.

Pages 86-87: Electrolysis of Brine

1 a)   sodium chloride in water *[1 mark]*

b)   product 1: sodium hydroxide/NaOH *[1 mark]* collected at B *[1 mark]*
product 2: chlorine/Cl_2 *[1 mark]* collected at A *[1 mark]*

It doesn't matter which way round you put these two products, as long as you have the right product linked to the right location.

c) i)   Half-equation: $2H^+ + 2e^- \rightarrow H_2$
[2 marks available — 1 mark for correct reactants and products, 1 mark for correct balancing]
What happens: Two hydrogen ions accept two electrons to become one hydrogen molecule *[1 mark]*

  ii)   Half-equation: $2Cl^- \rightarrow Cl_2 + 2e^-$
[2 marks available — 1 mark for correct reactants and products, 1 mark for correct balancing]
What happens: Two chloride ions each lose an electron and become one chlorine molecule *[1 mark]*.

2 a)   17% *[1 mark]*

b) i)   chlorine/Cl_2 *[1 mark]*

  ii)   sodium hydroxide/NaOH *[1 mark]*

  iii)   sodium hydroxide/NaOH *[1 mark]*

c)   chlorine/Cl_2 *[1 mark]*, sodium hydroxide/NaOH *[1 mark]*

d)   chlorine/Cl_2 *[1 mark]*

How to get answers for the Practice Papers

You can print out answers for the Practice Papers by accessing your free Online Edition of this book.

There's more info about how to get your Online Edition at the front of this book.